Science 4
Learning Coach Guide

Part 2

About K12 Inc.

K12 Inc., a technology-based education company, is the nation's leading provider of proprietary curriculum and online education programs to students in grades K–12. K¹² provides its curriculum and academic services to online schools, traditional classrooms, blended school programs, and directly to families. K12 Inc. also operates the K¹² International Academy, an accredited, diploma-granting online private school serving students worldwide. K¹²'s mission is to provide any child the curriculum and tools to maximize success in life, regardless of geographic, financial, or demographic circumstances. K12 Inc. is accredited by CITA. More information can be found at www.K12.com.

978-1-60153-339-5

Printed by RR Donnelley, Kendallville, IN, USA, May 2016

Table of Contents

Learning Coach Guide
Lesson 1: Classifying Animals

Invertebrates are organisms that don't have a backbone. The world of invertebrates is a fascinating one, as you'll see in *Come Learn With Me: Animals Without Backbones: Invertebrates.*

Invertebrates are very different from vertebrates. Most important, they don't have a backbone, whereas vertebrates do. Explore how invertebrates are grouped in the Kingdom Animalia, and discover the world of invertebrates.

Lesson Objectives

- Explain that living things are sorted into different groups based on certain common characteristics.
- State that *vertebrates* are organisms that have a backbone.
- State that *invertebrates* are organisms that do not have a backbone.
- Recognize that invertebrates are not a single taxonomic group but are represented in many groups.

PREPARE

Approximate lesson time is 60 minutes.

Advance Preparation

- You will need the book *Animals Without Backbones: Invertebrates,* by Bridget Anderson, for all the lessons in this unit. If you have not yet received the book, skip to unit 7.

Materials

For the Student

Come Learn with Me: Animals Without Backbones: Invertebrates by Bridget Anderson

Keywords and Pronunciation

anemone (uh-NEH-muh-nee)

Arthropoda (AHR-thruh-pah-duh) : The phylum of invertebrate animals, including insects and spiders, that have an exoskeleton, jointed legs, and a segmented body. More than 80 percent of all living species are arthropods.

Aurelia aurita (aw-REEL-ee-uh aw-RIY-tuh)

cell : The basic unit of all living things. There are many different types of cells in a living thing, each with a different job to do.

Chordata (kor-DAH-tuh)

classification : the process of dividing things into groups according to their characteristics

Cnidaria (niy-DAIR-ee-uh) : The phylum of aquatic, invertebrate animals that includes jellyfish and sea anemones.

exoskeleton (EK-soh-skeh-luh-tuhn) : The hard, outside body covering of an arthropod. The exoskeleton of the lobster protects the animal from predators in the ocean.

insect : An arthropod with three pairs of jointed legs and three body segments. Ants, grasshoppers, and mosquitoes are all insects.

---

invertebrate : An animal without a backbone. Sea stars, segmented worms, and spiders are classified as invertebrates because they don't have a backbone.

Kingdom Animalia : One of the six main groups into which all living things are divided. Most organisms in the animal kingdom are capable of movement, contain a nervous system, and take in food to produce energy.

phyla (FIY-luh) : Large groups of organisms that share similar characteristics. Phyla are the primary divisions within any kingdom. The singular of phyla is phylum.

phylogenetic (fiy-loh-juh-NEH-tihk)

species (SPEE-sheez) : A group of organisms that have many characteristics in common. The smallest and most specific groups that animals can be divided into are called species.

vertebrate (VUR-tuh-bruht) : An animal with a backbone. Mammals, fish, and birds are classified as vertebrates because they have a backbone.

TEACH

Activity 1: Let's Read! (Online)

Instructions

Have your student read pages 6-13 to learn about different types of invertebrates.

Activity 2: Invertebrate Hunt (Online)

Instructions

Have your student search for any invertebrates that live near you. If the weather is not appropriate for outdoor searching, have her use the websites to find invertebrates that may live in your environment. Encourage her to find as many as possible.

Safety

As always, you may wish to preview any websites before your student views them.

ASSESS

Lesson Assessment: Classifying Animals (Offline)

Students will complete an online assessment based on the lesson objectives. The assessment will be scored by the computer. The attached answer key is the most current and may not coincide with previously printed guides.

Learning Coach Guide
Lesson 2: The World of Sponges

Sponges aren't just for cleaning. In nature, sponges are animals that live in water. Learn the parts of a sponge, and discover the sponge's capababilities.

Lesson Objectives

- Identify characteristics of sponges (they have the ability to regenerate damaged parts, they reproduce through budding, and they live only in water).
- Identify the parts of a sponge (ostium, canal, osculum, and flagellum).

PREPARE

Approximate lesson time is 60 minutes.

Materials

> For the Student
>> Come Learn with Me: Animals Without Backbones: Invertebrates by Bridget Anderson
>> 📖 Sponges
> For the Adult
>> 📖 Sponges Answer Key

Keywords and Pronunciation

budding : A method of reproduction in which pieces of a sponge break off and develop into new sponges. A sponge produces many spores and regenerates through budding.

flagella (fluh-JEH-luh) : Tail-like structures on a cell that move back and forth. The flagella pushed the water through the canal of the sponge.

larva : The early life stage of certain animals that are not fully developed. When the egg of an insect hatches, the larva emerges.

osculum (AHS-kyuh-luhm) : A large pore through which filtered water leaves the body of a sponge. Sponges pump water through the canal of the sponge and out through the osculum.

ostium : The tiny pores, or holes, on the outer layer of a sponge. The ostium on the outer layer of the sponge allows water to enter into the canal of the sponge.

Porifera (paw-RIF-uhr-uh) : The phylum of the simple, invertebrate animals called sponges. The barrel sponge, vase sponge, and red beard sponge are part of the phylum Porifera.

regenerate : To grow back or repair parts that have been damaged. Sponges have the ability to regenerate body parts that may have been damaged by a predator.

spicules (SPIH-kyools) : Tiny fibers or minerals that make up the skeleton of a sponge. Within the jelly-like layer of a sponge cell is a network of needle-like spicules that form the skeleton of the sponge.

TEACH

Activity 1: Let's Read! *(Online)*

Instructions
Have your student read pages 14 to 17 to learn about the world of sponges.

Activity 2: The Parts of a Sponge *(Online)*

ASSESS

Lesson Assessment: The World of Sponges (*Online*)

Students will complete an online assessment based on the lesson objectives. The assessment will be scored by the computer. The attached answer key is the most current and may not coincide with previously printed guides.

Name _____ Date _____

Sponges Answer Key

1. Using the words in the Word Bank, label the parts of the sponge.

Word Bank				
canal	flagella	osculum	ostia	spicule

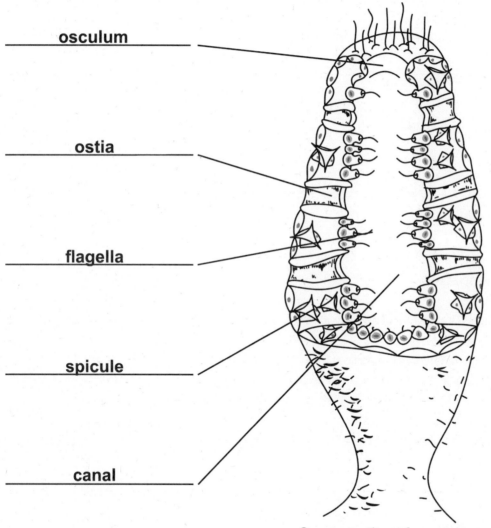

_____ **osculum** _____

_____ **ostia** _____

_____ **flagella** _____

_____ **spicule** _____

_____ **canal** _____

Cross section of a sponge

2. Use the words above to describe how water enters and exits the
   sponge's body cavity._____**answers will vary**_____

   _____

   _____

Learning Coach Guide
Lesson 3: Cnidarians

Jellyfish, sea anemones, and coral are but a few of the animals that make up the phylum Cnidaria. Cnidarians have tentacles with stinging cells at the end that are used to fight off predators, help feed the cnidarian, and help it sense the environment.

Lesson Objectives

- Identify a characteristic of cnidarians (they have tentacles with stinging cells).
- Identify medusa and polyp as the two common body types of cnidarians.
- Identify the three functions of tentacles (to sting predators, sense the environment, and bring food into the animal's mouth).
- State that most cnidarians help build up coral reefs.

PREPARE

Approximate lesson time is 60 minutes.

Materials

For the Student

Come Learn with Me: Animals Without Backbones: Invertebrates by Bridget Anderson

🖳 Cnidaria Chart

For the Adult

🖳 Cnidaria Chart Answer Key

Keywords and Pronunciation

anemone (uh-NEH-muh-nee)

Cnidaria (niy-DAIR-ee-uh) : The phylum of aquatic, invertebrate animals that includes jellyfish and sea anemones.

medusa : A body form of cnidarians. Medusae float freely through the water.

mutualism (MYOO-chuh-wuh-lih-zuhm) : A relationship between two animals in which both animals benefit. Clownfish and sea anemones live together to help each other survive. This relationship is known as mutualism.

polyp (PAH-luhp) : A body form of cnidarians. A polyp attaches to rocks, shells, or the sea floor by its feet-like structures.

TEACH
Activity 1: Let's Read! *(Online)*

Instructions

Have your student read pages 18 to 23 to learn about cnidarians--water creatures once known as stinging nettles.

Activity 2: Characteristics of Cnidarians *(Online)*
Instructions
Print the Cnidaria Chart if you have not already done so. Have your student use her book to complete the chart.

ASSESS
Lesson Assessment: Cnidarians (*Online*)
Students will complete an online assessment based on the lesson objectives. The assessment will be scored by the computer. The attached answer key is the most current and may not coincide with previously printed guides.

TEACH
Activity 3: Search for Cnidarians *(Online)*
Instructions
Print the Activity Instructions if you have not already done so.

Name _____   Date _____

Cnidarian Chart

Complete the missing parts of the chart.

1. SEA ANEMONE

How It Looks:
**has tentacles, looks like a plant
or flower**

How It Moves:
it waves from the ocean floor

Where It Lives:
in salt water

Something That Makes It Unique:
**Sometimes it thinks clownfish are
part of its own body**

2. JELLYFISH

How It Looks:
**some look like umbrellas, and
some look like lion manes**

How It Moves:
floats and pulses in the water

Where It Lives:
salt water

Something That Makes It Unique:
**Turtles eat them even though
they get stung.**

3. HYDRA

How It Looks:
tiny, with tentacles

How It Moves:
it makes somersaults

Where It Lives:
in fresh water

Something That Makes It Unique:
they can stand on their tentacles

4. STONY CORAL

How It Looks:
made of polyps in colonies

How It Moves:
moves gently on the ocean floor

Where It Lives:
in salt water

Something That Makes It Unique:
**new corals grow on top of old
ones**

Learning Coach Guide
Lesson 4: The Diverse World of Worms

Worms are diverse organisms that belong to three different phyla. Earthworms, flatworms, and roundworms are some of the worms that inhabit our world.

Lesson Objectives

- Identify characteristics of roundworms (they bend from side to side to move, have nostrils but no eyes).
- Compare segmented worms to roundworms and flatworms.
- Identify a characteristic of segmented worms (their body is made up of many ring-like segments).
- Identify characteristics of flatworms (they have eyespots and the ability to regenerate when damaged).
- State that the term *worm* is used for animals in three different phyla.

PREPARE

Approximate lesson time is 60 minutes.

Materials

For the Student

Come Learn with Me: Animals Without Backbones: Invertebrates by Bridget Anderson

🖳 Characteristics of Worms Chart

For the Adult

🖳 Characteristics of Worms Answer Key

Keywords and Pronunciation

Annelida (A-nluh-duh) : The phylum of invertebrate animals that includes earthworms and all other segmented worms. Earthworms, bristle worms, and leeches are part of the phylum Annelida.

cuticle : The protective layer of skin on worms. The muscles of a roundworm are covered with a skin that produces a tough layer called the cuticle.

ganglion (GANG-glee-uh) : A simple, brain-like organ in some animals. In a flatworm, the eyespots are connected to the ganglia, which process information from the eyespots.

Nematoda (NEH-muh-toh-duh) : The phylum of invertebrate animals that includes roundworms. Nematoda live wherever ther is water.

planarian (pluh-NAIR-ee-uhn) : A nonparasitic flatworm that lives in freshwater. A planarian, a type of flatworm, can regenerate its body even when it has been cut into many pieces.

Platyhelminthes : The phylum of invertebrate animals that includes more than 20,000 species of flatworms. Platyhelminthes means flat worm in Greek.

TEACH
Activity 1: Let's Read! *(Online)*
Instructions
Have your student read pages 24 to 29 to learn about worms.

Activity 2: Characteristics of Worms *(Offline)*
Instructions
There are many kinds of worms in different habitats all over the world. We can find worms deep in the oceans, in ponds, in soil, and many other places. Use the chart and the book to compare the characteristics of worms mentioned in the book.
Safety
As always, you may wish to view recommended websites before your student views them.

ASSESS
Lesson Assessment: The Diverse World of Worms *(Online)*
Students will complete an online assessment based on the lesson objectives. The assessment will be scored by the computer. The attached answer key is the most current and may not coincide with previously printed guides.

TEACH
Activity 3. Optional: A Visit to Worm World *(Online)*

Name _____   Date _____

Characteristics of Worms Chart

The worms listed below belong to different phyla, so they have similarities as well as differences. Use pages 24-29 of the text to find the specific characteristics of each type of worm. Look at the characteristics listed below, then decide which characteristics apply to each worm. Write "yes" in the chart if the worm has the characteristic; write "no" if it does not. Three have been completed for you.

Characteristics	Worms		
	Roundworms	Flatworms	Segmented Worms
Eyespots connected to ganglia	No	Yes	No
Able to regenerate if their body is damaged	No	Yes	Some do
Long, slender, round bodies	Yes	No	Yes
Flat bodies	No	Yes	No
Segmented bodies	No	No	Yes
Nostrils	Yes	No	No
Head and tail	Yes	Yes	Yes
Bend from side to side in order to move	Yes	Yes	No

Use the information in the chart to compare segmented worms to roundworms and flatworms.

_____

_____

_____

_____

_____

Learning Coach Guide
Lesson 5: Mighty Mollusks

Snails and slugs are mollusks. So are squid. Learn what these very diverse animals have in common.

Lesson Objectives

- Identify characteristics of mollusks (they have a soft body, a thick skin called a mantle, and a foot for movement).
- Identify three ways mollusks can move (using a foot extended from their body, filling their shell with air to float away, pulling with their arms, or taking water in and pushing it out of the siphon).
- Identify characteristics of snails and slugs (they have stalked eyes, antennae, radula, and a foot on the underside of the belly for movement).
- Identify characteristics of clams, mussels, and oysters (they have two shells joined by a hinge, a siphon, and a foot for movement).
- Identify characteristics of octopuses and squids (they have a large brain, highly developed eyes, and long arm-like appendages).

PREPARE

Approximate lesson time is 60 minutes.

Materials

For the Student

Come Learn with Me: Animals Without Backbones: Invertebrates by Bridget Anderson

🖳 Mollusca Crossword Puzzle

For the Adult

🖳 Mollusca Crossword Answer Key

Keywords and Pronunciation

bivalve : A mollusk that has two shells connected by a hinge. Clams have two shells connected by a hinge, so they are bivalves.

cephalopod (SEH-fuh-luh-pahd) : A mollusk that can swim and has appendages on its head. An octopus can swim and has tentacles, so it is a cephalopod.

gastropod (GAS-truh-pahd) : A mollusk that has a foot attached to its underbelly. Most gastropods, including snails, have a single spiral shell. Slugs have no shell at all.

mantle : A thick outer covering on a mollusk's body. In some mollusks, the mantle produces a shell.

Mollusca (muh-LUH-skuh) : The phylum of invertebrate animals that have a soft body, a muscular foot for movement, and a mantle. The oyster belongs to the phylum Mollusca.

radula (RA-juh-luh) : The tongue-like structure of many mollusks that is covered in a hard, tooth-like substance. When a mollusk feeds, its radula can remove algae from rocks.

siphon (SIY-fuhn) : In a bivalve, a tube used for breathing and feeding. A bivalve breathes and gets food by filtering the water that comes in through the siphon.

TEACH
Activity 1: Let's Read! *(Online)*
Instructions
Have your student read pages 30 to 35 to learn more about mollusks.

Activity 2: Mollusca Puzzle *(Offline)*
Instructions
There are a lot of mollusks--more than 50,000 species of them, in fact. Have your student review the characteristics of the phylum mollusca by solving the crossword puzzle.

ASSESS

Lesson Assessment: Mighty Mollusks (*Online*)
Students will complete an online assessment based on the lesson objectives. The assessment will be scored by the computer. The attached answer key is the most current and may not coincide with previously printed guides.

Name ______________________ Date ______________________

Mollusca Crossword Puzzle Answer Key

Use the clues on the next page to complete the puzzle.

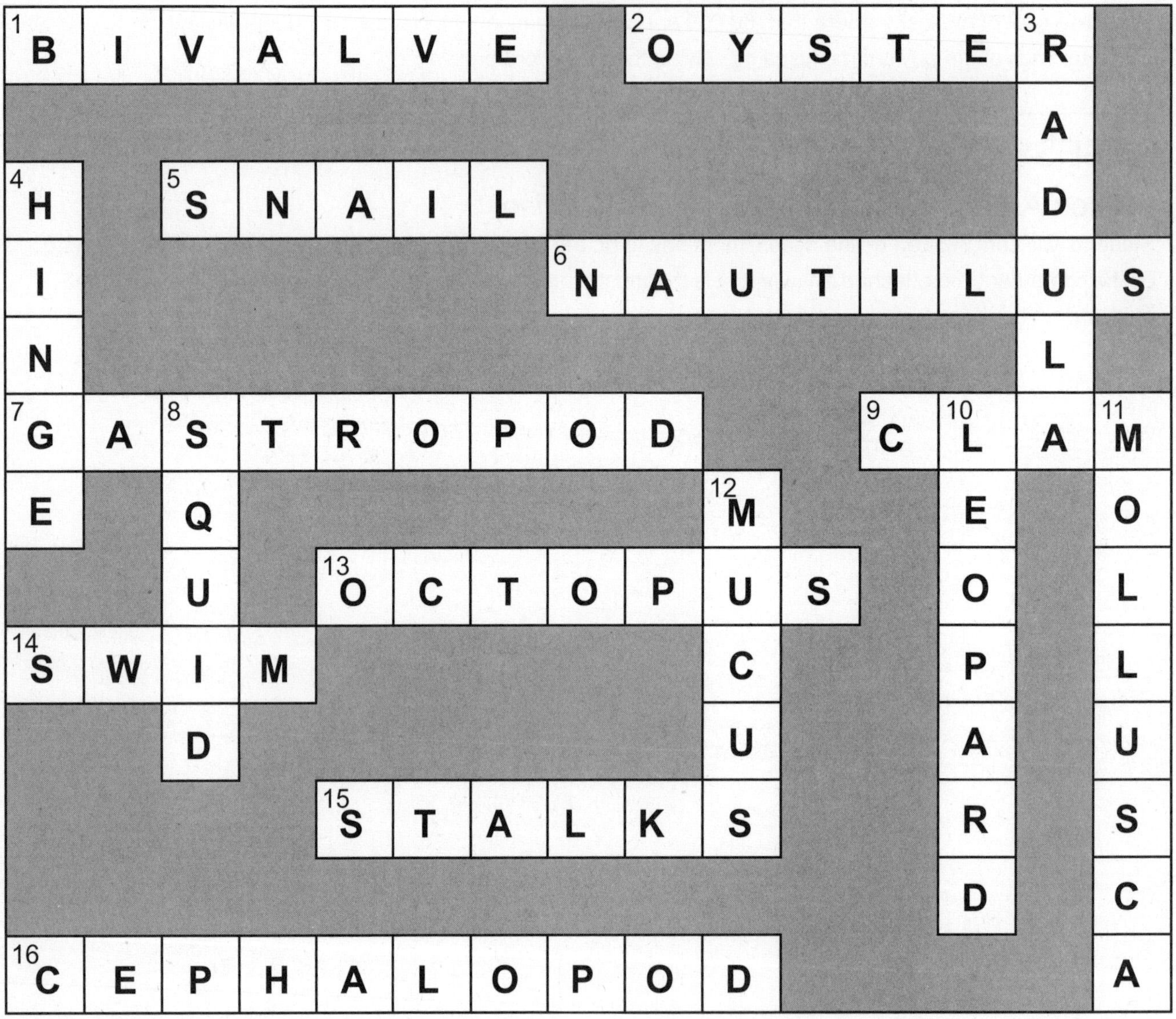
1 BIVALVE
2 OYSTER
3 RADULA
4 HINGE
5 SNAIL
6 NAUTILUS
7 GASTROPOD
8 SQUID
9 CLAM
10 LEOPARD
11 MOLLUSCA
12 MUCUS
13 OCTOPUS
14 SWIM
15 STALKS
16 CEPHALOPOD

Learning Coach Guide
Lesson 6: Arthropods

Arthropods are animals with a segmented body and jointed legs. They include spiders, crayfish, and millipedes. These animals actually have a lot in common, as the book will tell.

Lesson Objectives

- Identify common characteristics of arthropods (they have jointed legs, a segmented body, and an exoskeleton).
- Identify characteristics of insects (they have three pairs of legs, three body segments--head, thorax, and abdomen--and one or two pairs of wings).
- Identify characteristics of crustaceans (they have five pairs of jointed legs, two pairs of antenna, and an exoskeleton).

PREPARE

Approximate lesson time is 60 minutes.

Materials

> For the Student
>> Come Learn with Me: Animals Without Backbones: Invertebrates by Bridget Anderson
>> 🖥 Arthropods
> For the Adult
>> 🖥 Arthropods Answer Key

Keywords and Pronunciation

abdomen (AB-duh-muhn) : The rear body section of an arthropod. The abdomen is the back end of an insect.

Arthropoda (AHR-thruh-pah-duh) : The phylum of invertebrates, including insects and spiders, that have an exoskeleton, jointed legs, and a segmented body. You can easily recognize arthropods by their hard, outer covering, known as the exoskeleton, and by their jointed legs.

cephalothorax (seh-fuh-luh-THOR-aks) : In arachnids, the front section of the body that includes the head. An arachnid's antennae are on the cephalothorax.

chiton (KIY-tuhn)

crustacean (crustacea) (kruhs-TAY-shuhn)

entomologist (en-tuh-MAH-luh-jist)

exoskeleton (EK-soh-skeh-luh-tuhn) : The hard, outside body covering of an arthropod. The exoskeleton of the crab protects the animal from predators.

head : The top or front part of the body. All insects have three body parts: the head, the thorax, and the abdomen.

metamorphosis (meh-tuh-MOR-fuh-suhs) : The series of changes in body shape that certain animals go through as they develop from eggs to adults. The metamorphosis of a frog is from egg to tadpole to adult frog.

spinneret : An organ in some invertebrates, including spiders, that produces silk. The spinneret releases a liquid silk that the spider uses to weave a web.

thorax (THOR-aks) : The middle body section of many arthropods. The thorax of an arthropod lies between the head and the abdomen.

TEACH
Activity 1: Let's Read! *(Online)*

Instructions
Have your student read pages 36 to 41 to learn about arthropods, a phylum that includes insects and crustaceans.

Activity 2: What Makes Me an Arthropod? *(Offline)*

Instructions
Have your student complete the Arthropods worksheet. Encourage her to refer to the book as often as necessary.

ASSESS

Lesson Assessment: Arthropods (*Online*)

Students will complete an online assessment based on the lesson objectives. The assessment will be scored by the computer. The attached answer key is the most current and may not coincide with previously printed guides.

TEACH
Activity 3. Optional: A Visit to the Museum *(Online)*

Instructions
Print the Activity Instructions if you have not already done so.

Safety
As always, you may wish to preview recommended websites before having your student view them.

Arthropods Answer Key

1. Arthropods have three common characteristics. What are they?
   A. **hard exoskeletons**
   B. **jointed legs**
   C. **segmented bodies**

2. Insects and crustaceans are two classes of arthropods. Fill in the chart to find out the characteristics that make each class unique.

	Insects	**Crustaceans**
How many pairs of jointed legs do they have?	**3**	**5**
Their bodies are divided into what parts?	**head, thorax, and abdomen**	**head and thorax fused, abdomen**
Do some have wings?	**yes**	**no**
Do they have an exoskeleton?	**yes**	**yes**
Do they have antennae?	**yes**	**yes**

3. Label the body parts of the praying mantis and lobster.

head   thorax   abdomen

head and thorax   abdomen

Learning Coach Guide
Lesson 7: Echinoderms

Sea stars, sea urchins, sand dollars, and sea cucumbers are all part of the phylum Echinodermata, meaning *spiny skin* in Greek. Your student will take a closer look at these echinoderms and their common characteristics.

Lesson Objectives

- Identify characteristics of echinoderms (they are protected by hard plates, their body has radial symmetry, and they move by pumping water into their tube feet).
- Identify characteristics of sea stars (they live only in water, they have suction cups on their tube feet, their body has radial symmetry, and they are able to regenerate their body when it is damaged).

PREPARE

Approximate lesson time is 60 minutes.

Materials

For the Student

Come Learn with Me: Animals Without Backbones: Invertebrates by Bridget Anderson

📖 Sea Stars

For the Adult

📖 Sea Stars Answer Key

Keywords and Pronunciation

cephalothorax (seh-fuh-luh-THOR-aks) : In arachnids, the front section of the body that includes the head. An arachnid's antennae are on the cephalothorax.

crustacean (crustacea) (kruhs-TAY-shuhn)

echinoderm (ih-KIY-nuh-durm)

Echinodermata (ih-kiy-nuh-dur-MAH-tuh) : The phylum of aquatic invertebrates that are protected by a thick, spiny skin. Sea stars, sea urchins, and sand dollars are part of the phylum Echinodermata.

madreporite (MA-druh-por-iyt) : A small, circular plate that filters out debris. Water enters the madreporite on the top side of a sea star's central body and is pumped to the many feet on the bottom.

TEACH
Activity 1: Let's Read! (Online)

Instructions

Have your student read pages 42 to 45 to learn about echinoderms, a phylum of animals that have a spiny, symmetrical body.

Instructions

Have your student read pages 42 to 45 to learn about echinoderms, a phylum of animals that have a spiny, symmetrical body.

Activity 2: Sea Stars *(Online)*

Instructions

Print out the activity instructions and the Sea Stars sheet if you have not already done so. Have your student fill out the sheet. Encourage her to refer to the book as often as necessary.

ASSESS

Lesson Assessment: Echinoderms (*Online*)

Students will complete an online assessment based on the lesson objectives. The assessment will be scored by the computer. The attached answer key is the most current and may not coincide with previously printed guides.

TEACH

Activity 3. Optional: A Closer Look into the Ocean *(Online)*

Instructions

Print the Activity Instructions if you have not already done so. Encourage your student to click on every picture on the website.

Safety

As always, you may wish to preview recommended websites before your student views them.

Name _____   Date _____

Sea Stars Answer Key

Review the Reading

Use the questions below to guide you as you re-read pages 44 – 45.

1. In what environment would you find a sea star? **Echinoderms can be found in many different ocean environments. They are found in the shallow pools of the ocean as well as at the bottoms.**

2. What happened when fishermen found a sea star, chopped it up, and threw it back into the ocean? **The pieces that were cut off from the sea star grew into fully developed sea stars. Sea stars can regenerate their bodies when they are damaged.**

3. The body of a sea star has radial symmetry. What does this mean? **A sea star has a center part of its body where the appendages, or arms, grew out. The arms are evenly spaced around the center part of the body.**

4. Why is the sea star able to stay anchored on a rock, a coral, or the bottom of the ocean? **Sea stars have suction cups on the bottom of their tube feet that help them stay anchored.**

How a Sea Star Moves

On the website, view the movie clip titled "Sea Star Feeding." Then describe in your own words how a sea star moves. Refer to the reading as well as the text on the web page for help.
Answers will vary but should include that the sea star has tube feet along the bottom of its arms. There are suction cups at the bottom of the tube feet. The sea star takes in water through its madreporite and pushes it throughout its body, ending at the tube feet. By changing the pressure of water in its body, the sea star can move the tubed feet and thus move forward.

Learning Coach Guide
Lesson 8: Unit Review and Assessment

Your student will play a game and review what she learned throughout the unit. A unit assessment will follow the review activity.

Lesson Objectives

- Identify different groups of invertebrates (sponges, cnidarians, worms, mollusks, arthropods, echinoderms) according to their common characteristics.

PREPARE

Approximate lesson time is 60 minutes.

Materials

For the Student

⌨ Classification of Invertebrates Review Cards

Come Learn with Me: Animals Without Backbones: Invertebrates by Bridget Anderson

TEACH
Activity 1: Review the Reading (Offline)
Instructions

Have your student print the Classification of Invertebrates Review Cards. Cut out the cards along the dotted lines. (Answers and Questions are on separate cards.) Then have her follow the directions to play a Concentration game with them.

These are the correct matches:

Question: I am an echinoderm. My body has radial symmetry. In order to move, I pump water into my tube feet. What is on the outside of my body?

Answer: hard plates

Question: You can find me only in the water. I have nostrils but no eyes. I move through the water by bending my body from side to side. What am I?

Answer: roundworm

Question: I am a segmented worm. What makes me different from other worms?

Answer: segmented body

Question: If you look at me, you'll see that my body is divided into segments with jointed legs. My body is protected by an exoskeleton. What am I?

Answer: arthropod

Question: I have a soft body with a thick skin called a mantle covering me. I also have a foot for movement. What am I?

Answer: mollusk

Question: I have tentacles coming from my body, and they have long, stinging cells on the end. What am I?

Answer: cnidarian

Question: I am a type of worm that can regenerate a damaged body part when it is injured. I also have eyespots. What am I?

Answer: flatworm

Question: I am a sponge living deep in the ocean. I reproduce through budding. What else is common among sponges?

Answer: can regenerate a body part if it becomes damaged

Activity 2: Invertebrate Organisms (Online)

Instructions

Encourage your student to refer to the book as often as necessary as she goes online to look at marine invertebrates and answer questions.

ASSESS

Unit Assessment: Classification of Invertebrates (Online)

Students will complete an online assessment of the objectives covered so far in this unit. The assessment will be scored by the computer. The attached answer key is the most current and may not coincide with previously printed guides.

TEACH

Activity 3. Optional: ZlugQuest Measurement (Online)

Learning Coach Guide
Lesson 1: Electric Charges and Magnetic Poles

All of us have had contact with electricity. We come into a room and turn on a light. We use a flashlight. We see lightning bolts. We also have experience with magnetism--our refrigerators stay closed using magnets, and many motors are loaded with them. Learn how these two things--electricity and magnetism--are related.

Electricity and magnetism are related phenomena. A good way to get started is to look at the connection between electric charge and the structure of the atom.

Lesson Objectives

- Recognize that objects with the same electrical charges repel and objects with different electrical charges attract.
- Describe the Earth's magnetic field and identify magnetic north and south.

PREPARE

Approximate lesson time is 60 minutes.

Materials

For the Student

- 📖 Electric Discoveries: Your Scientist Notebook
- 📖 Come Here! Go Away!

   bar magnets, pair

   fabric, wool cloth

   household item - clothes hanger

   balloon (2)

   string

For the Adult

- 📖 Come Here! Go Away! Answer Key

Lesson Notes

Electricity is a common enough phenomenon to most students. The 101 plugged-in appliances in almost every house all involve electricity. While the student may not realize it, a bolt of lightning, the annoying way hair clings to a comb with little crackling noises, or how socks come out of the dryer stuck to shirts are also due to electricity. Perhaps most surprising of all, a refrigerator magnet sticking to a refrigerator is also related! Scientists think of magnetism and electricity as related, and call the two together *electromagnetism*.

In this lesson and others to follow, the student will learn how electricity works, how magnetism works, and how these two seemingly different things are the same; and finally, how we use electromagnetism to build very useful devices--such as every motor in your house, from the hair dryer to the VCR.

In this lesson the student will use a simplified picture of an atom. While scientists know that real atoms are more complicated than the one pictured, this is still a useful teaching model:

- In the center of the atom is the nucleus. The nucleus is so small that if a single atom were the size of New York City, the nucleus would be about the size of a raisin sitting in the middle of town.
- The nucleus is made of two different kinds of particles known as neutrons and protons. The proton has a positive electrical charge. The neutron has no charge.
- Moving around the nucleus of the atom are electrons, here modeled as particles, too. Electrons have a negative electrical charge, and are smaller than protons and neutrons.

[The names of these particles can help the student remember their charges. Protons are positive. Neutrons are neutral.]

An atom that has the same number of electrons and protons is electrically balanced. As a whole it is neither positive nor negative.

The number of electrons in an atom can change. If an atom loses an electron, the atom will have a net positive charge. If an atom gains an electron, the atom will have a net negative charge.

You can remove electrons from an object with something as simple as a wool rag. If you rub a balloon with wool, you can rub electrons off the atoms in the rag and onto the balloon, leaving the wool with a net positive charge. The balloon will have a net negative charge. The more you rub, the more electrons get moved (up to a point!).

If you rub two balloons this way, the two balloons push each other apart. The further apart the balloons, the less they push on each other. The wool rag, on the other hand, attracts both balloons, and the closer the rag is, the more the rag attracts a balloon. This reflects very basic principles about charged objects (including electrons and protons): like charges repel each other, opposite charges (positive on one, negative on the other) attract each other, and the closer the charged objects are, the stronger the push or pull.

This explains why clothes stick to each other in the dryer--some pieces lose electrons in the tumbling process, while others gain them, so some have a net negative charge, and some a net positive charge. Opposites attract.

Magnets show some of the same behaviors as the charged balloons, although the charges on the balloons don't seem to affect the magnets directly. Two magnets brought close to each other might push each other away, or pull themselves together, and the closer they are, the stronger the push or pull. However, there's no "magnetic charge." You'll never find two magnets that JUST push each other, or just pull. Every magnet has two ends, labeled "North" and "South." When you bring two like ends together, the magnets push on each other; when you bring two unlike ends together, the magnets pull on each other.

Keywords and Pronunciation

atom : A tiny particle that is the fundamental building block of any substance. The properties of an atom determine the properties of an element made up of only those atoms.

electron : A tiny part of an atom with a negative electrical charge. In an atom, electrons form a cloud around the nucleus.

proton : A tiny part of the nucleus of an atom, which has a positive electrical charge. The number of protons determines the chemical properties of the atom.

TEACH
Activity 1: Opposites Attract *(Online)*
Instructions

Have your student read through the Explore on his own. Reinforce and explain difficult concepts as needed.

Explore Suggestions:

Check your student's understanding by asking the following questions:

1. What causes an object to become electrically charged? (the movement of negatively charged particles from one object to another)

2. How do objects with opposite charges react to one another? (they attract)

3. How do objects with like charges react to one another? (they repel)

Screen 3:

Punch holes out of red and blue construction paper to represent atomic particles. Assign charges to the colors or have your student talk in terms of red and blue. Have your student place the same amount of holes on different objects around the room to show that those objects are neutral. Have him transfer only one color of "particles" to other objects to show electrical charges transferring. Discuss which objects would attract or repel. For example, Objects with more blue will attract objects with more red, and so on.

Screen 4:

Explain that attracting and repelling has nothing to do with charges "liking" or "not liking" each other. It is a result of forces between the charged objects.

After this activity, check to see if your student can:

- Recognize that objects with the same electrical charges repel and objects with different electrical charges attract.

If your student has difficulty with any of these concepts, you may wish to review the Explore with him and have him explain the key points on each screen.

Activity 2: Electric Discoveries: Your Scientist Notebook *(Offline)*
Instructions

Teaching:

Discuss the importance of good record-keeping in science. What could happen as a result of not keeping good records? How could this cause problems in the science community? What if, for example, two different people make an important scientific discovery?

What to Expect:

Your student will be prepared to make his own detailed Scientist Notebook over the course of the unit Electricity and Magnetism.

Activity 3: Come Here! Go Away! *(Offline)*

Instructions

Teaching:

Review that an object with a "charge" has either an excess or deficit of electrons. A surplus of electrons creates a negative charge. A deficit of electrons creates a positive charge.

If your student has trouble understanding how transferring electrons creates either a positive or negative charge, see the Explore Suggestion for Screen 3.

Troubleshooting:

Perform this activity in a dry area. You may have trouble on a humid day or in a humid location. Instead of wool, you can use silk or hair.

What to Expect:

Your student should be able to explain that opposite charges attract, like charges repel, and magnets have poles that attract and repel as well. Check to see that your student used the words *repel* and *attract* in his answers and describes these facts correctly in the Scientist Notebook section of the activity.

Safety

Do not use magnets near the computer.

ASSESS

Lesson Assessment: Electric Charges and Magnetic Poles (*Online*)

Students will complete an online assessment based on the lesson objectives. The assessment will be scored by the computer. The attached answer key is the most current and may not coincide with previously printed guides.

Name _____ Date _____

Come Here! Go Away! Answer Key

Rubbing two neutral objects causes electrons to move off one object and onto another.

* A negatively charged object has more negatively charged particles (electrons).
* A positively charged object has less negatively charged particles (less electrons).

Materials
Balloons, 2
String
Wool cloth
Bar magnets

Attracting
1. Tie the balloon to string and hang it in a place you can reach. (You may want to suspend it from a coat hanger).
2. Hold the cloth near the balloon.
3. Nothing happens. Why? They are both neutral.
4. Rub the balloon quickly with the cloth. You are rubbing electrons off the cloth and onto the balloon right at this moment!
5. Hold the cloth near the balloon. Write what you observe. _____

   The cloth and balloon attract to each other.
   _____

Come Here! Go Away! Answer Key

Draw the positive and negative charges on the balloon and cloth before and after you rubbed the balloon.

Key

+ means positive

- means negative

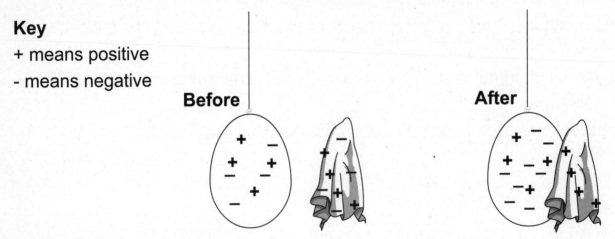

Before

After

Drawings may vary, but should include the key idea that before the balloon is rubbed there are equal numbers of "+" and "-" charges. After the balloon is rubbed the numbers are different.

Repelling

1. Tie a new balloon to string and hang it near the first balloon.

2. Rub both balloons with the cloth.

3. Place the balloons near each other. Write what you observe. _____
   The balloons repel one another.

Draw the charges on the balloons using the same key as before.

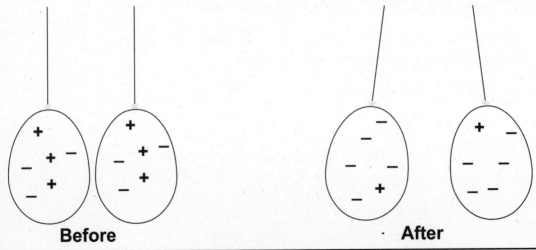

Before

After

Come Here! Go Away! Answer Key

Magnetism

Magnets have poles always in pairs that repel and attract. Investigate repelling and attracting with the magnets by placing their ends near each other. Then, label the poles in the illustrations.

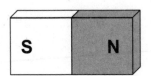 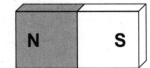 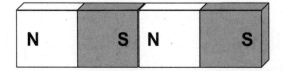

Repelling   **Attracting**

Key:

N = North pole

S = South pole

Your Scientist Notebook

On a separate piece of paper, make your first electricity and magnetism entry in your Scientist Notebook. Write the date so you have a record of your notes. Then make careful entries for your balloon experiments and your magnet experiments. Imagine someone else was going to read your notes and try to do the same experiments you did, to see if they get the same results.

Do you need to repeat your experiments in different ways to make sure you know what is happening? Draw any diagrams you may need in order to explain your findings.

Learning Coach Guide
Lesson 2: Magnet Madness

There are magnets all around us in motors, cabinets, and elsewhere, but how do they work? Students will begin to understand how magnets work, as well as the concept of the Earth as a magnet.

Lesson Objectives

- Describe the Earth's magnetic field and identify magnetic north and south.
- Explain how to construct a temporary magnet.
- Explain that lightning is produced as a result of static discharge.

PREPARE

Approximate lesson time is 60 minutes.

Materials

For the Student

    💻 Find Yourself

      bar magnets, pair

      household item - compass

      sewing needle

      bowl

      cardboard - float (foam, cork)

      water

Lesson Notes

Magnets are quite common, but how do they work? Your student may have asked questions such as: Why are magnets made of metal and not wood? Why do magnets stick to the refrigerator door and not to my shirt? Why do magnets attract some kinds of metal and not others?

This lesson will continue your student's exploration with different kinds of magnets, how they work, and what phenomena they cause.

In our simplified model of an atom, electrons orbit the nucleus. In addition, each of these electrons spins on its own axis like a tiny whirling ball. To explain magnetism without going into too many details, a *charge in motion* creates its own magnetic direction or "field." Because the electrons are little charges and are in motion, each electron behaves like a tiny magnet. This means that objects are full of tiny magnetic fields. In most objects, however, these spins and fields all have different orientations--that is, they all point different ways. Like a crowd in which everyone is saying something different, the overall effect is that you can't really hear anyone. But in some materials, such as iron, the electrons can line up so that all their magnetic fields point in the same direction. That is something like a crowd speaking one word or phrase all at one time. When the electrons in an object line up, the entire object takes on a single, large magnetic field. It becomes a magnet.

Bar magnets, horseshoe magnets, and any other magnets that stay magnetized for a long time and don't need to be turned on to work are called *permanent magnets.* You can demagnetize a permanent magnet by heating it or even by simply striking it with a hammer, because these actions knock the electrons out of alignment. There are also naturally occurring magnetic substances, such as magnetite, which is commonly called *lodestone.* Magnetite is a permanent magnet.

Temporary magnets are magnets that gain and lose their magnetism quickly. If you wrap a piece of nonmagnetic iron in a copper wire and send a small amount of electricity through the wire, the iron will become magnetic. The iron remains magnetic only as long as it is enveloped in an electrical field.

The Earth itself is an enormous magnet. Its magnetic field is generated by the motion and interactions of liquid and solid metals thousands of miles underneath the surface. A magnetic field from the Earth extends from the magnetic north pole to the magnetic south pole in the same way a magnetic field surrounds a bar magnet the size of your hand.

Because the Earth itself is a magnet, other magnets will interact with it. That is how a compass works: the needle is a small magnet that aligns itself with Earth's magnetic field. The magnetic north and south poles are the two ends of the giant magnet that is our planet. They need not be the same places exactly as the geographic poles--and, in fact, they are not. [Technically, what we conventionally call the North Pole is a *south pole*, since that pole of the Earth's magnet attracts the north part of the needle magnet! No matter - we always call that part of the Earth the North Pole.]

- The (conventionally called) magnetic north pole of Earth is about 1,400 km from the geographic North Pole.
- The magnetic south pole is 2,750 km from the geographic South Pole.

A compass, therefore, doesn't actually point toward the geographic North Pole--it points toward the magnetic north pole. For a captain at sea this is an important difference; for hiking a trail, this is not as important.

Keywords and Pronunciation

atom : A tiny particle that is the fundamental building block of all substances. The properties of an atom determine the properties of an element made up only of those atoms.

aurora australis (uh-ROR-uh AW-struh-luhs)

aurora borealis (uh-ROR-uh bor-ee-A-luhs) : Lights seen at night in northern latitudes caused by electrically charged particles from the sun.

magnetic field : The magnetic effect every magnet creates in the space around it. The Earth has a very large magnetic field.

magnetic pole : A region of a magnet where the magnetic field is especially strong. All magnetic poles are either north or south poles. In a bar magnet, the poles are at the ends.

TEACH
Activity 1: Magnificent Magnets *(Online)*
Instructions

Have your student read through the Explore on his own. Reinforce and explain difficult concepts as needed.

Explore Suggestions:

Check your student's understanding by asking these questions:

1. What is the difference between a permanent and temporary magnet? (A permanent magnet keeps its magnetism. A temporary magnet can lose it or have it turned on and off.)

2. What particles must line up in order for an object to be magnetic? (electrons)

3. Tell why the biggest magnet on Earth is the Earth itself. (Because of its huge iron core surrounded by liquid metal, and because of its spinning motion, a huge magnetic field is created that surrounds Earth.)

After this activity, check to see if your student can:

- Describe the Earth's magnetic field and identify magnetic north and south.
- Explain how to construct a temporary magnet.

If your student has difficulty with any of these concepts, you may wish to review the Explore with him and have him explain the key points on each screen.

Activity 2: Mapping with Magnets (Offline)

Instructions

Teaching

Explain that you can magnetize an iron object either with electricity or by rubbing a magnet across it. Rubbing an iron object with a magnet causes the electrons in the object to line up so that their motion is all in the same direction. This creates a magnetic field that surrounds the iron object. Have your student explain this as he magnetizes the needle.

If needed, discuss the four cardinal directions: north, south, east, and west.

Troubleshooting:

Before using the compass, move away from large metal objects such as the computer. The compass will point to it instead of the magnetic north pole. Use a large bowl and small float. Be sure your student rubs the needle with the north side of the magnet so the needle points north.

What to Expect:

Your student should be able to explain how to make a temporary magnet, including what happens to the electrons in a piece of iron as it is magnetized.

Answers:

The needle became magnetic when you rubbed it with a magnet. The electrons in the needle are forced to line up so that their motions are in one direction. This creates a single, large magnetic field.

Activity 3: Scientist Notebook (Offline)

Instructions

Teaching:

Encourage your student to write detailed notes in his notebook. Remind him of the importance of keeping accurate records. Refer him to the Explore activity if needed. Have your student keep track of the entries he is making in the Scientist Notebook. He will need them at the end of the unit.

Troubleshooting:

If your student did not perform the activity, have him go back and do so.

What to Expect:

Your student should be able to write about each item listed. He should understand how electrons are affected when he rubs the needle with the magnet.

Helpful Hints:

The sun rises in the east.

The sun sets in the west.

ASSESS

Lesson Assessment: Magnet Madness (Offline)

Students will complete an offline assessment based on the lesson objectives. Print the assessment and have students complete it on their own. Use the answer key to score the assessment, and then enter the results online. The attached answer key is the most current and may not coincide with previously printed guides.

Name _____   Date _____

Magnet Madness Assessment Answer Key

1. Tell how to make a temporary magnet using electricity. _____
   Wrap a piece of iron with copper wire and send
   electricity through the wire.
   _____

2. Tell how to make a temporary magnet without electricity. _____
   Rub a piece of iron or steel with a magnet.
   _____
   _____

3. Describe what happens to electrons in an iron object when the
   object is magnetized. _____
   Magnetizing an object causes its electrons to line up
   so that their motions are all in the same direction. This
   creates a strong magnetic field and makes the object
   magnetic.

4. Tell what scientists think makes Earth a magnet. _____
   Because of its huge iron core surrounded by liquid
   metal and its spinning motion, a huge magnetic field is
   created that surrounds Earth.
   _____

Magnet Madness Assessment Answer Key

5. Draw lines to show the Earth's magnetic field. Label the approximate
   locations of the magnetic north and south poles.

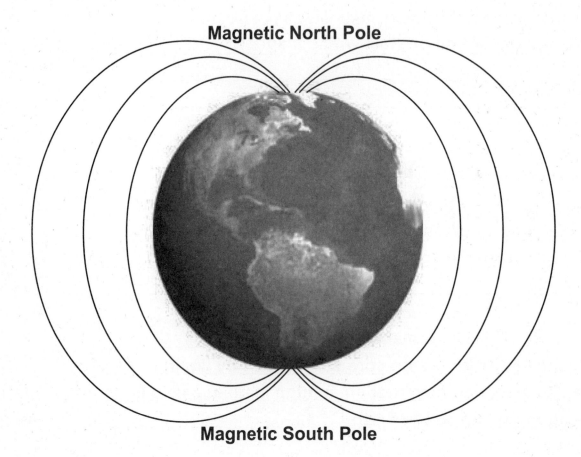

Learning Coach Guide
Lesson 3: Static Electricity - Truly Shocking

Static electricity could have been called *unbalanced-charge electricity* since it arises from the separation of postive and negative charges. But a bolt of lightning is enough to make anyone aware that static electricity is part of our everyday lives.

Lesson Objectives

- Explain that friction can build up static electrical charges when two objects are rubbed together and transfer electrons from one surface to the other.
- Recognize that *static electricity* is the buildup of electrical charges on an object.
- Explain that lightning is produced as a result of static discharge.
- Recognize that *electric current* is the flow of electrons through a wire.

PREPARE

Approximate lesson time is 60 minutes.

Materials

For the Student

   📖 Action Static

    household item - comb

    household item - puffed rice

    household item - wool sweater or cloth

    balloon

    water - (sink)

   📖 Get a Charge from an Electroscope

    jar - glass

    index cards, 4" x 6"

    paper clip - large

Lesson Notes

Static electricity is electricity that builds up on surfaces, rather than flowing through a wire. Common examples of static electricity include clinging clothes, hair sticking to a dry comb, and even lightning itself. It might have been called *unbalanced-charge electricity*, because it results from the separation of charged particles.

Electric lights, ringing doorbells, and all the motors in your house--from the one keeping the refrigerator cool to the one that spins clothes in the dryer--are the result of *circuit electricity*. Think of this as *flowing electrical charge*.

- *Circuit electricity* - The flow of electrical charge, for example, through wires.
- *Static electricity* - The separation of charges resulting in unbalanced charge.

Both of these result from the movement of electrons, so they might be spoken of as different types of electron movement. It is easiest to think in terms of wires and surfaces.

Three ways to build up static charge are:

- *Friction* - Rubbing two objects together causes electrons to move from one object to another.
- *Induction* - An electrically neutral object is brought near to--but does not touch--a charged object. The charged object doesn't donate electrons, but makes electrons move in the neutral object. The new arrangement of electrons in the neutral object can make different parts appear charged.
- *Conduction* - In this process, one charged object directly donates its charge to another object.

Sooner or later, a redistribution of charges will take place, leading to electrical stability once more. Extra charges may move slowly off a charged object, perhaps into the air. They may also move off all at once. Either case is known as *static discharge*.

A balloon rubbed against your head will stick to a wall. Gradually, though, it will pass charges over to the wall and, as it loses its electrical imbalance, the electrical force that is making it cling will diminish. The balloon will fall.

Your student has felt a rapid static discharge every time she gets a shock when reaching for a metal doorknob. Your student's body becomes charged when she walks across a rug (most likely). The charge imbalance is redressed when the student touches the knob, by a quick flow of electric charge from finger to knob, sometimes with a spark.

Keywords and Pronunciation

conduction : The application of an electric charge to an object by direct contact with a charged object. The glass rod got its electric charge by conduction.

friction : Rubbing two objects together to create an imbalance of charges. Friction was part of the reason I got shocked when I touched the doorknob.

induction : The application of an electric charge to an object through the nearness of a charged object. The glass globe got its electric charge by induction.

static electricity : Electricity on the surface of objects, better thought of as unbalanced-charge electricity. Lightning is the huge discharge of static electricity charge from a cloud.

TEACH
Activity 1: More Than Just a Shock *(Online)*
Instructions

Have your student read through the Explore on his own. Reinforce and explain difficult concepts as needed.

Explore Suggestions:

Check your student's understanding by asking the following questions:

1. Name three different ways static charges can build up on an object. (conduction, induction, friction)

2. During a storm, an electrical imbalance can occur. What is the effect when that imbalance tries to balance itself with a static discharge? (lightning)

After this activity, check to see if your student can do the following:

- Explain that friction can build up static electrical charges when two objects are rubbed together and transfer electrons from one surface to the other.
- Recognize that static electricity is the buildup of electric charges on an object.
- Explain that lightning is produced as a result of static discharge.

If your student has difficulty with any of these concepts, you may wish to review the Explore with him and have him explain the key points on each screen.

Activity 2: Action Static *(Offline)*
Instructions
Teaching:

Discuss prior experiences with static electricity. Has your student ever touched something metal and gotten a shock? Has he combed his hair and noticed that his hair keeps sticking out toward the comb or brush? These are examples of static electricity. They happened because of a buildup of charges--on his body in the case of a shock, or on the comb when his hair continues to stick up.

Answers:

Examples of static electricity may vary. Some examples include the following:

1. Hearing crackling noises while combing your hair.

2. Clothes sticking to each other in the dryer.

3. Static discharge causing lightning in the sky.

Troubleshooting:

Static electricity demonstrations are best done in colder, low-humidity weather. Water vapor in humid weather can carry away electrical charges, so they will not build up on the objects.

For the best effect in Activity 2, make sure the balloon is fully inflated. The tighter the balloon skin, the better.

What to Expect:

Activity 1 - The comb becomes charged with electrons from the wool cloth. It attracts the stream of neutral water. It attracts the negative charges in the water.

Activity 2 - The puffed rice will jump away from your student's finger. After you charge the balloon, the neutral puffed rice is attracted to the negative charges. The puffed rice then picks up some of the negative charges by conduction. When your finger touches the balloon, static discharge builds up on your finger. Your finger and the puffed rice have the same negative charges and the rice is repelled.

Activity 3: Electroscope *(Online)*
Instructions
Teaching:

Review conduction and induction. *Conduction* occurs when an object transfers charges to another object by touching it. *Induction* occurs when a neutral object is brought close to, but does not touch, a charged object.

Troubleshooting:

If the paper clip does not work, use copper wire. You will need copper wire later in the unit as well. Remember that static electricity activities are best done in a cold, dry environment.

What to Expect:

The leaves of the aluminum foil will separate. The transfer of negative electrical charges from the balloon will cause foil to build up similar charges. Similar charges repel. Eventually all the charge from the balloon will be discharged and it will no longer be able to charge the electroscope. You can recharge the balloon with the wool.

Answer:

Conduction

Scientist Notebook:

Check your student's diagram for the following:

· Transfer of negative charges (minus sign) from the balloon to the electroscope

· Buildup of negative charges on the aluminum-foil leaves

· Separation of the aluminum-foil leaves

ASSESS

Lesson Assessment: Static Electricity - Truly Shocking (*Offline*)

Students will complete an offline assessment based on the lesson objectives. Print the assessment and have students complete it on their own. Use the answer key to score the assessment, and then enter the results online. The attached answer key is the most current and may not coincide with previously printed guides.

Lesson Assessment Answer Key

Static Electricity - Truly Shocking

Answers:

1. static electricity

2. Rubbing two objects together, such as two from the list, will cause electrons to be rubbed off one object and onto another, creating an electric charge buildup.

3. Answers may vary but should include the following key information: Lightning occurs when electrical charges that are not balanced become balanced with a static discharge. A shock happens the same way. When charges build up on a person and the person touches an object, static discharge and a shock occur.

Learning Coach Guide
Lesson 4: Electric Currents

Static electricity is the electricity of unbalanced charges. *Electic current,* as a general rule, is electricity of moving charges. Your student is most familiar with this kind of electricity. Electrical power comes to the house via outside wires and lights the lights in the house and makes all the kitchens utilities run. But what is current electricity and what does it have to do with electrons?

Lesson Objectives

- Identify the parts of a circuit: battery, light, wire, and switch.
- Differentiate between a *series circuit* and a *parallel circuit.*
- Recognize that *electric current* is the flow of electrons through a wire.
- State that electric currents flow easily through materials that are conductors and do not flow easily through materials that are insulators.

PREPARE

Approximate lesson time is 60 minutes.

Advance Preparation

- One site you may use to purchase the 4.5v battery is www.campmor.com. If you choose not to purchase one, 2 D size batteries will work for the experiment in lieu of the 4.5v battery. Make sure you place them with positive and negative ends facing each other.
- Save the completed circuit for use in the next lesson.

Materials

For the Student

   🖳 Build a Circuit

   electrical tape

   electrical wire, plastic coated - 2 feet

   light bulb holders (3)

   light bulbs, miniature (5)

   battery - 4.5 V (D cell can work)

   brads (2)

   cardboard

   knife

   paper clip

   scissors

⌨ Make an Electric Quiz Board

hole punch

light bulb - small

light bulb holder

wire, copper - 3 meters

battery - D cell or 4.5 volt

cardboard - sturdy, 33 cm x 30 cm

crayons 8 - for decorating (optional)

paper clips - metal (14)

tape, masking

Lesson Notes

The electrical energy that runs all sorts of devices, from computers to radios to washing machines, comes from electric charges running through wires. In a handheld flashlight the wire is inside the casing, connected to a battery. For a television set, wires are plugged into a wall socket, attaching it to a long series of other wires that lead ultimately to a power station. The basic mechanism, though, is the same: electric charge flowing through wires.

This is very different from static electricity discussed before.

Static electricity, as we have seen, occurs when some electrons are pulled off one object and put on another. The result is separated charges--a positively charged sock, for example, clinging to a negatively charged T-shirt.

An electric current occurs when electric charges (electrons in wires, for example) move from one place to another.

In metals such as copper, not all the electrons are attached to particular atoms. These are called *free electrons*, because they are shared among the huge number of copper atoms.

In a copper wire, free electrons actually move pretty slowly one by one. Mostly they "push" the other free electrons in front of them, so that as electrons are pushed in at one end, others pop off at the other. In this way, electrical charge moves through the wire.

What gives electrons a push? A battery is one example. A battery has two terminals. If the two terminals are connected by a wire, it allows charges that have built up on one terminal to move through the wire to the other terminal. As this happens, a chemical reaction in the battery speeds back up again to keep pushing more charge onto the terminals.

A *circuit* is any connection of batteries and other devices with wires. Circuits usually have *switches*, which simply allow (*closed* switch) or stop (*open* switch) the flow of charges through a wire. Circuits can be very complicated, but it's useful to know about two simple types:

· *Series circuit*--A type of circuit in which the electrical charge flows from one point to another in only one path.

· *Parallel circuit*--A type of circuit in which the electrical charge can flow in more than one path from one point to another.

Keywords and Pronunciation

electric current : The flow of electrons through a wire.

TEACH
Activity 1: Electric Currents *(Online)*

Instructions

Have your student read through the Explore on his own. Reinforce and explain difficult concepts as needed.

Explore Suggestions:

Check your student's understanding by asking the following questions:

1. True or False: In order to have electric current, you need a continuous flow of protons. (False. You need a continuous flow of charge, usually electrons).

2. Explain the difference between electric current and static electricity. (Electric current is moving charges. Static electricity is the result of unbalanced charges that do not move).

3. What is the name of a circuit in which electric current flows from one point to another through more than one path? (parallel)

4. How do switches control electricity? (A switch can open or close a circuit, either blocking charges or letting charges flow freely.)

Screen 6:

Use symbols to draw a circuit diagram. You can do this by hand or with a computer drawing program. Have your student illustrate a series and parallel circuit. For information on symbols used to make these diagrams, visit the Science, Technology, and Engineering Site or the teaching guide site listed in the Lesson Resources. After this activity, check to see if your student can do the following:

- State that electric currents flow easily through materials that are conductors and do not flow easily through materials that are insulators.
- Identify the parts of a simple circuit: battery, light, wire, and switch
- Differentiate between series and parallel circuits.

If your student has difficulty with any of these concepts, you may wish to review the Explore with him and have him explain the key points on each screen.

Activity 2: Build a Circuit *(Offline)*

Instructions

Teaching:

Eleccrtric current is electricity that flows through wires or fluids. Electricity between two points flows differently in series and parallel circuits. In a *series circuit*, electricity can flow in only one path. A *parallel circuit* provides more than one path down which electricity can flow. A *switch* is a device that is used to control the flow of electricity. A switch that is turned to ON is called *closed* and completes a circuit and allows electric current to flow. A switch that is turned to OFF is called *open* and breaks the circuit.

Troubleshooting:

Closely supervise your student during this activity. You can use two D batteries in place of the 4.5-volt battery. Make sure you place them with positive and negative ends facing each other. Use caution, as bulbs may get hot. Extra bulbs are provided if any blow out.

Tips:

Save the completed circuit for use in the next lesson.

What to Expect:

Series circuit: Removing one bulb will cause the other to go out.

Parallel circuit: Removing one bulb will not make the other bulb go out.

Answers:

1. The circuits were complete when the bulbs were lit.

2. The bulbs in the parallel circuit were brighter than the bulbs in the series circuit.

3. Unscrewing the bulb in the series circuit caused the other to go out. Unscrewing the bulb in the parallel circuit does not make the other go out.

4. In a series circuit, electricity flows in one path. In a parallel circuit, electricity has more than one path to flow through.

5. Older holiday lights were put in a series circuit. They were improved by using a parallel circuit instead.

Safety

The bulbs may be hot. Use a cloth or oven mitt to unscrew them.

ASSESS

Lesson Assessment: Electric Currents (*Offline*)

Students will complete an offline assessment based on the lesson objectives. Print the assessment and have students complete it on their own. Use the answer key to score the assessment, and then enter the results online. The attached answer key is the most current and may not coincide with previously printed guides.

TEACH

Activity 3. Optional: Make an Electric Quiz Board (*Offline*)

Instructions

Teaching:

If needed, review that electricity can flow in a closed circuit. You will need to assist your student in making the quiz board.

What to Expect:

The quiz board will light up when the student touches a question and the correct answer with a paper clip.

Name _____   Date _____

Lesson Assessment Answer Key

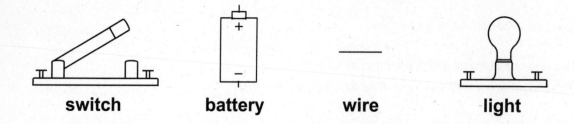

switch   **battery**   **wire**   **light**

1. Draw a series circuit. You may refer to the icons above to help you sketch each part.

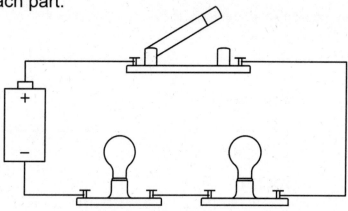

2. Draw a parallel circuit. You may refer to the icons above to help you sketch each part.

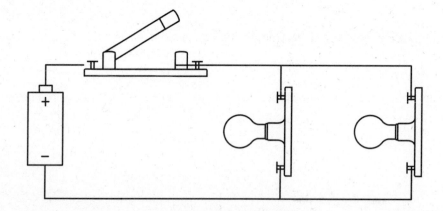

Lesson Assessment Answer Key

3. What happens if a bulb is removed from a series circuit? Why? _____

The other bulb goes out. Electricity flows in just one path in a series circuit. Removing the bulb opens the circuit and cuts off the electrical flow.

4. What happens if you remove a bulb is removed from a parallel circuit? Why?

The other bulb remains lit. Electricity can flow in more than one path in a parallel circuit so removing one bulb does not affect the flow.

5. To produce an electric current, you need a continuous source of _____.

Ⓐ electrons
B. protons
C. watts
D. static

Learning Coach Guide
Lesson 5: Resistance, Conductors, Insulators

Resistance, insulation, and conduction all describe how a material lets charge flow through it. Circuits are often made up of several materials, so the flow of charge through a circuit depends on these properties.

Lesson Objectives

- State that electric currents flow easily through materials that are conductors and do not flow easily through materials that are insulators.
- Give examples of conductors and insulators.
- Describe how certain materials affect the flow of electricity through a wire.
- State that electric current produces magnetic fields and that an electromagnet can be made by wrapping a wire around a piece of iron and then running electricity through the wire.

PREPARE

Approximate lesson time is 60 minutes.

Advance Preparation

- You will need to save your circuit set-up for the next lesson. For the Fruity Electricity activity, you can purchase a copper screw and zinc screw at a home repair center.

Materials

For the Student

🖥 Conductors and Insulators

coin

drinking glass

household item - 2 ft - covered wire

household item - 4.5 volt battery

household item - bulb holder

household item - small lightbulb

plastic

rubber band

aluminum foil

paper clip

paper, notebook

pencil

tape, clear

household item - 1 copper screw about 5 cm

household item - 1 holiday light

household item - 1 zinc screw about 5 cm

household item - lemon

Lesson Notes

The examples of electrical charge flowing in circuits so far considered have assumed copper wire, which is the most common material used. Other kinds of materials, however, also allow electrical charge to flow to greater or lesser degrees.

- *Conductivity* is the ability of a electrical charge to flow through a substance.
- Materials that allow electrical charge through easily are said to be *good conductors.*
- Some materials have perfect electrical conductivity under certain conditions. These materials are called *superconductors.*

Superconductors are not easy to make, but are now widely used in certain kinds of equipment like medical scanners.

Water conducts electricity well. This has dangerous consequences. If you drop an electric appliance in the bath tub or by the sink, you may find yourself part of a circuit involving the appliance, water, and plumbing, and get a dangerous shock!

Materials that carry electrical current poorly are called *insulators.* Insulators are used for the following reasons:

- To keep the charge from leaving the wire, except where it should
- To keep other charges away from a wire
- To protect people who work with electrical equipment

The rubber coating on wires acts as electrical insulation, and many electrical devices are covered in glass or clay ceramics for the same reason.

In an insulator, there are few free electrons to "push" others, unlike in copper wire. An electrical charge, therefore, cannot flow easily through it.

When a charge moves down a wire it meets with *resistance.* Different materials resist electric charge by different amounts. The bars inside a toaster heat up because they are made of material that resists the flow of electric charge. The electrons run into many more static atoms than in the copper wire, and as they run into them they make the atoms start vibrating faster. This makes the material heat up. This is great for toasting bread!

The filament inside a light bulb glows because it is made of material that resists the flow of electrical charge, too. If the filament were a superconductor--that is, if it had no resistance at all--the light bulb would not give off light.

Keywords and Pronunciation

conductor : Any material through which electricity can flow. A copper wire is a good conductor of electric charge as it flows through the circuit.

insulator : A substance that cannot conduct electricity very well. The rubber casing around the speaker wire serves as an insulator for the electrical current.

resistance : A measure of how strongly a substance opposes the flow of electricity. The unit of resistance in an electric circuit is the ohm.

TEACH
Activity 1: More About Circuits (Online)
Instructions
Have your student read through the Explore on his own. Reinforce and explain difficult concepts as needed.

Explore Suggestions:

Screen 1: Have your student look around the room for places where electricity is being used. Can he see the wires that bring the electricity from the source? Are the wires bare or coated?

Check your student's understanding by asking the following questions.

1. What are the meanings of the words *conductor, insulator,* and *resistance?* (conductor: any material through which electricty can flow easily; insulator: a substance that conducts electricity very poorly; resistance: a measure of how strongly a material opposes the flow of electricity)
2. Name some conductors. (copper wire, gold, aluminum, and water)
Name some insulators. (glass, rubber, and wood)
3. What happens when a good conductor is used in a circuit? (Electric charges are allowed to flow easily down the wire.)
4. Why add an insulator to the outside of a wire? (It makes the wire safer to use.)

If your student has difficulty with any of these concepts, you may wish to review the Explore with him and have him explain the key points on each screen.

Activity 2: Conductors and Insulators (Offline)
Instructions
Teaching: Review the effects of conductors and insulators in electric circuits. Conductors allow electrons to flow easily. Insulators slow down electrical flow.

Lab Safety: Bulbs may get hot.

What to Expect:

The bulb will light up only if the gap in the circuit is bridged with a conductor. The aluminum foil, paper clip, and coin will conduct electricity. The bulb will not light if the glass, pencil, paper, and rubber are used to complete the circuit.

Answers:

Make sure your student adds his conclusions from this experiment to the other data he has collected in his Scientist Notebook. Check that his conclusions match his data from his tests.

Safety
Bulbs may get hot.

ASSESS

Lesson Assessment: Resistance, Conductors, Insulators (*Online*)
Students will complete an online assessment based on the lesson objectives. The assessment will be scored by the computer. The attached answer key is the most current and may not coincide with previously printed guides.

TEACH
Activity 3. Optional: Fruity Electricity *(Online)*
Instructions

Teaching: Fruits contain electrolytes--chemical solutions that contain many ions. Ions can be positively or negatively charged. When the two different metal plates are put into the lemon, negative particles move toward one plate while positive particles move toward the other. If you connect them with a conductor, a current will flow.

What to Expect: Attaching metal plates and wires to the fruit will light the bulb.

Learning Coach Guide
Lesson 6: Electromagnetism

The production of magnetic effects by electric current and the production of electric current by moving magnets show the close connection between electricity and magnetism. This connection allows for the construction of electromagnets, which are the basis of generators and motors.

Lesson Objectives

- State that electric current produces magnetic fields and that an electromagnet can be made by wrapping a wire around a piece of iron and then running electricity through the wire.
- Recognize that electromagnets are used in electric motors, generators, and other devices, such as doorbells and earphones.
- Describe how to increase or decrease the strength of an electromagnet.

PREPARE

Approximate lesson time is 60 minutes.

Advance Preparation

- You will need to save your copper wire for the electromagnet investigation in this lesson.

- One site you may use to purchase the 4.5v battery is www.campmor.com. If you choose not to purchase one, 2 D size batteries will work for the experiment in lieu of the 4.5v battery. Make sure you place them with positive and negative ends facing each other.

Materials

For the Student

- The Strongest Electromagnet

    battery - 4.5 volt

    copper wire

    nail, iron - not rusty

    paper clip - 20

Lesson Notes

It wasn't until the 19th century that people noticed the connection between electricity and magnetism. If your student wonders why people didn't always know that electricity and magnetism are connected, you might take a moment to think about how someone would figure this out. Do lightning and lodestones seem to have anything to do with each other?

In 1820, a Danish scientist named Hans Christian Oersted noticed that a compass that had been left sitting next to a length of wire changed the direction of its needle when an electric charge was sent through the wire. When the electricity was turned off, the needle went back to its original position.

Today this experiment can be run by anyone with a battery, a compass, and some wire. But at the time it was revolutionary--electricity and magnetism were found to be connected. People, including Andre-Marie Ampere in France, began working to figure out what the connection was, and many more discoveries were made. The term *electromagnetism* was given to the combined phenomena of electricity and magnetism.

A temporary magnet created by the flow of electricity is known as an *electromagnet*. The more current, the more powerful the electromagnet. Enormous electromagnets are used at construction sites and junkyards to lift up entire cars. As soon as the electricity is turned off, the huge piece of iron at the end of the crane ceases to be a magnet, and the car falls from it into a designated place.

A moving magnet can also push charges through a wire. Make a coil out of some copper wire. Connect the ends to a meter that shows the strength of an electric current. Pass a magnet back and forth through the coil. The meter will react, showing that an electric charge is being made to flow in the wire just by passing the magnet in and out of the coil. Visual images explaining this are given in the lesson.

If the magnet is kept steady and the coil of wire moved instead, you have the basic mechanism behind an electric generator.

Keywords and Pronunciation

electromagnet : A temporary magnet made using electric current, usually running around a metal core.

Hans Christian Oersted (hahns KREES-tyahn OUR-sted)

TEACH

Activity 1: Electromagnetism *(Online)*

Instructions

Have your student read through the Explore on his own. Reinforce and explain difficult concepts as needed.

Explore Suggestions:

Check your student's understanding by asking these questions:

1. What are the three parts of an electromagnet? (iron core, wire, battery or source of electric current)

2. Why is an electromagnet called a "temporary magnet"? (Because the magnetism can be turned off when the electricity is turned off.)

3. How does an electromagnetic operator release metal attached to an electromagnet? (The operator turns off the electricity.)

4. Name some uses for electromagnets. (doorbells, motors, generators, earphones)

After this activity, check to see if your student can:

- State that electric current produces magnetic fields and that an electromagnet can be made by wrapping a wire around a piece of iron and then running electricity through the wire.
- Recognize that electromagnets are used in a variety of everyday devices, including electric motors and generators, as well as simple machines such as doorbells and earphones.
- Describe how to increase or decrease the strength of an electromagnet.

If your student has difficulty with any of these concepts, you may wish to review the Explore with him and have him explain the key points on each screen.

Activity 2: The Strongest Electromagnet *(Offline)*

Instructions

Teaching:

Electric current can be used to produce a magnetic field. Using electricity to create a magnet creates a temporary magnet. Ask your student what will happen as soon as the electricity is turned off. (Answer: the magnetism will be turned off as well.)

Troubleshooting:

Move well away from the computer and any wet areas before doing this experiment.

What to Expect:

Your student should understand that wrapping the nail with more coils will create a stronger magnetic field. The nail with the most coils will pick up the most paper clips.

Answers:

Accept any reasonable hypothesis.

Check that your student's observations and graph match.

Check your student's Scientist Notebook:

Question 1: The likely reason Annabelle's electromagnet was stronger was that she wrapped it with more coils of wire.

Question 2: Battery strength will also have an effect on the strength of an electromagnet. Your student may describe an experiment testing battery strength.

Safety

Move well away from the computer and any wet area before doing this experiment.

ASSESS

Lesson Assessment: Electromagnetism (*Offline*)

Students will complete an offline assessment based on the lesson objectives. Print the assessment and have students complete it on their own. Use the answer key to score the assessment, and then enter the results online. The attached answer key is the most current and may not coincide with previously printed guides.

TEACH

Activity 3. Optional: Electrical Safety (*Online*)

Instructions

Teaching:

Discuss some reasons why one must be careful with electricity. Electric shock can be painful and even deadly. Look for areas that may not be electrically safe. Point out areas that have been made specifically safe with regard to electricity.

What to Expect:

Your student should become familiar with ways of interacting safely with electricity.

Name _____   Date _____

Electromagnetism Assessment

1. If you wrap a wire around a piece of iron, and then run electricity through the wire, what happens to the iron? **It becomes magnetized.**

   _____

   _____

   _____

2. Read this data from an experiment. Then state which electromagnet was wrapped with the most coils.   **Laura's electromagnet**

   Electromagnet Tests:
   Laura's electromagnet: 12 paper clips
   Rachel's electromagnet: 5 paper clips
   Ethan's electromagnet: 7 paper clips

3. Circle the objects that use an electromagnet.

   (Motor)   (Doorbell)   Scissors   (Earphones)

   Bicycle gears   (Generator)   Mechanical pencil

4. Electromagnets are used at junk yards to lift and move giant pieces of metal from one place to another. What happens to the magnetism and the huge pieces of metal as soon as the electricity is switched off?

   There is no more magnetism and the pieces of metal fall to the ground.

   _____

Learning Coach Guide
Lesson 7: Unit Review and Assessment

Review electricity and magnetism. Enjoy a presentation from your student about what he has learned through his investigations during this unit. Take the unit assessment.

Lesson Objectives

- Recognize that objects with the same electrical charges repel and objects with different electrical charges attract.
- Explain how to construct a temporary magnet.
- Explain that friction can build up static electrical charges when two objects are rubbed together and transfer electrons from one surface to the other.
- Identify the parts of a circuit: battery, light, wire, and switch.
- State that electric currents flow easily through materials that are conductors and do not flow easily through materials that are insulators.
- Recognize that electromagnets are used in electric motors, generators, and other devices, such as doorbells and earphones.
- Demonstrate that magnets have two poles (north and south) and that like poles repel each other while unlike poles attract each other.
- State that electric currents produce magnetic fields and that an electromagnet can be made by wrapping a wire around a piece of iron and then running electricity through the wire.
- Differentiate between series and parallel circuits.
- Describe the earth's magnetic field and identify magnetic north and south.
- Describe the Earth's magnetic field and identify magnetic north and south.
- Demonstrate mastery of the important knowledge and skills of this unit.
- Differentiate between a *series circuit* and a *parallel circuit*.
- State that electric current produces magnetic fields and that an electromagnet can be made by wrapping a wire around a piece of iron and then running electricity through the wire.

PREPARE

Approximate lesson time is 60 minutes.

Materials

    For the Student

        🖳 Posters and Presenting: Be A Modern Day Faraday

        household item - assorted art supplies

        tape, adhesive

        cardboard - or posterboard

        markers

        paper, construction, 9" x 12"

        paper, notebook

TEACH
Activity 1: Electric Obstacle Course (Online)
Instructions
Have your student read through the Electric Obstacle Course and answer the questions. Have him go back through the lessons if needed to review difficult concepts.

Activity 2: Be a Modern Day Faraday (Offline)
Instructions
Teaching:

Review concepts from the list if needed. Provide enough time for your student to complete the poster. Encourage your student to use the notes he made during the unit. Review his notebook to make sure it is in a form that your student can use. While your student presents the poster, act as if he is an expert and ask him questions about the unit that he should be able to answer.

Troubleshooting:

This activity may take longer than 20 minutes. Allow your student enough time to review before the assessment.

What to Expect:

Your student should be able to demonstrate accurate understanding of concepts related to the list of topics for his poster. He should be able to communicate those results and answer questions.

ASSESS

Unit Assessment: Electricity and Magnetism (*Online*)
Students will complete an offline Unit Assessment. Print the assessment and have students complete it on their own. Use the answer key to score the assessment, and then enter the results online. The attached answer key is the most current and may not coincide with previously printed guides.

TEACH
Activity 3. Optional: ZlugQuest Measurement (Online)

Name _____   Date _____

Electricity and Magnetism Assessment Answer Key

Circle the correct answer.

1. Two objects are rubbed together, creating friction. What will likely happen next?
   A. Protons will be rubbed from one surface to another.
   (B) Electrons will be rubbed from one surface to another.
   C. A flow of electricity will start.
   D. The two objects will cool down.

2. Electric current flows easily through a _____.
   A. charger
   B. resistance
   C. volts
   (D) conductor

3. You can make an iron nail magnetic by wrapping it in wire and sending electricity through the wire.
   (A) True
   B. False

Use the words in the Word Bank to fill in the blanks. You may not need to use all of the words.

protons	neutrons	electrons	switch
battery	wire	light	iron core
insulator	resistance		

4. When an object is negatively charged, it has more
   ___**electrons**___ than ___**protons**___.

5. You can make a simple series circuit by connecting a
   ___**battery**___, ___**switch**___, ___**light**___, and ___**wire**___.

6. An ___**insulator**___ is a material through which electricity does not flow freely.

Electricity and Magnetism Assessment Answer Key

7. Draw charges on the balloons to show them attracting.

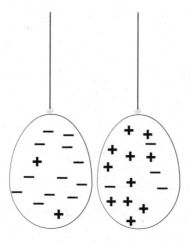

8. Draw charges on the balloons to show them repelling.

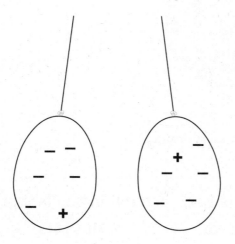

Electricity and Magnetism Assessment Answer Key

9. Draw two sets of bar magnets. Show one pair attracting.
   Show one pair repelling. Label the north and south
   poles correctly.

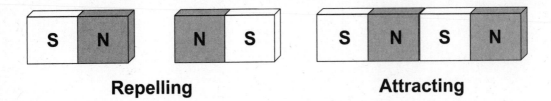

Repelling   **Attracting**

10. Draw lines to show the Earth's magnetic field.
    Label the location of the magnetic north and south poles.

Magnetic North Pole

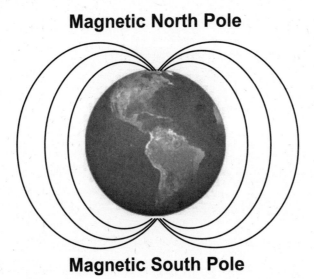

Magnetic South Pole

11. A needle rubbed with a magnet becomes magnetic. Is this a
    temporary or permanent magnet? _____**temporary**_____

12. What do scientists think makes Earth a giant
    magnet? **The Earth has a huge, solid core made partly of**
    metal, surrounded by liquid also made in part of metals.
    Because all of this spins around, scientists think a
    magnetic field is created that surrounds and protects Earth.

Electricity and Magnetism Assessment Answer Key

13. Label the battery, switch, lamp, and wire in each circuit below.

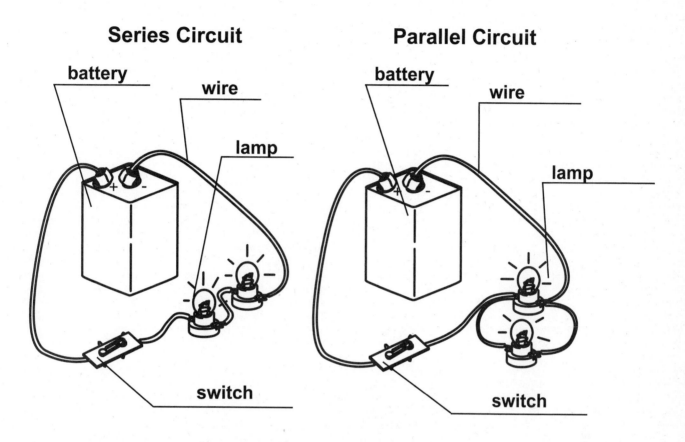

Series Circuit

battery

wire

lamp

switch

Parallel Circuit

battery

wire

lamp

switch

14. What would happen to the other light if you removed
one of the bulbs from a series circuit? Explain. **The other light**
would go out. Removing the bulb cuts off the flow of electric
current, because a series circuit has only one path to flow through.

15. What would happen to the other light if you removed
one of the bulbs from a parallel circuit? Explain. _____
Nothing. A parallel circuit has more than one path for electric
current to flow through.

16. Name two devices that use electromagnets. _____
Answers may vary but should include: motors, generators,
earphones, and doorbells.

Learning Coach Guide
Lesson 1: Rocks and Minerals

A simple rock might not look like much. Look closer, however, and you will see that it is formed from smaller substances--minerals. Where do minerals come from? What are they made of? Discover the answers to these questions, and learn how the birth of rocks is related to two awesome phenomena in nature--volcanoes and earthquakes.

The Earth is a planet that has characteristics unlike any other planet in our solar system. Life abounds on Earth partly because of the deep internal structure of the Earth. Through time, continents have shifted and slid across the Earth's surface. The materials that make up the Earth are varied, too, from sparkling minerals to huge rocks.

Lesson Objectives

- Identify the four main layers of the Earth and describe their characteristics.
- Explain that rock is composed of different combinations of minerals.

PREPARE

Approximate lesson time is 60 minutes.

Advance Preparation

- In this Science activity, your student will be using the rock kit for the first time. For the first few lessons in this unit she should not know the identity of the different rocks and minerals. Remove the lid with the key from the box, and set it aside for later reference.

Materials

For the Student

    📠 Rock Samples

    K12 Rocks and Minerals Kit

    magnifying glass

    paper, notebook

    pencil

Lesson Notes

The Earth has four main layers: inner core, outer core, mantle, and crust. These layers are not always sharply defined. The mantle and crust, for example, have a wide transition zone between them. These layers tell much about how the structure of the Earth affects all life.

The Inner and Outer Core

The Earth is about 12,700 kilometers (7,900 miles) in diameter, so the distance from surface to center is about 6,300 kilometers (3,900 miles). At the center is the inner core, made almost entirely of extremely hot, solid iron--about 4,500°C (8,130°F). At the surface, iron that hot would be liquid, but the inner core is under such intense pressure that the iron there is a solid ball. The inner core weighs 100 million million million tons and has 30 times more mass than the moon. Surrounding the inner core, which is about 2,400 kilometers (1,500 miles) in diameter, is the second layer--the outer core. This core is also mostly iron, but in a liquid state. This molten iron flows around in the depths of the Earth. The core of the Earth is hot because of the radioactivity left over from its formation. One theory is that the entire solar system formed at one time in a single series of processes that resulted in the accumulation of interstellar gases and dust.

The Mantle

The next layer nearer the surface of the Earth is the *mantle*. About 84 percent of the Earth's volume is in the mantle. This layer is rich in iron, aluminum, silicon, and oxygen. It is 700 km (about 430 miles) thick and has a temperature of about 1,500°C (2,730°F). The mantle is solid rock, but it is under such high pressure that it moves constantly. The shifting of the mantle is called *plastic movement*.

The Mohorovicic Discontinuity

Between the mantle and the crust lies a transition zone called the *Mohorovicic Discontinuity*, or the *moho* for short. This zone was discovered in 1909 by Andrija Mohorovicic, a Croatian seismologist. This layer is about 35 kilometers (22 miles) below the surface, and marks the upper part of the mantle and the bottom layer of the crust.

The Crust

The crust is the outermost layer of Earth. There are two main types of crust--continental and oceanic. The continental crust is less dense than the oceanic crust. It has high levels of the element silicon. Continental crust can float on magma (molten rock), so huge sections, or plates, of continental crust gradually move around the surface of the globe. The oceanic crust is located mainly under the ocean. It is composed of 50 percent silicon dioxide--the same substance that makes up sand. This part of the crust is constantly submerging into the mantle and then being created anew at ocean rifts. No part of oceanic crust is more than 200 million years old. The Earth's crust contains many minerals. Minerals often form as crystals--solid substances whose atoms are arranged in repeating patterns. Minerals have four defining characteristics: They form primarily in the Earth's crust, they are solids, they have a definite chemical composition, and they do not come from living things.

Igneous, Sedimentary, and Metamorphic Rock

Thousands of different kinds of rock exist on Earth. They may be made of minerals, glass, and organic matter. They are classified in three categories. *Igneous rocks* form from cooling magma--the molten rock under the surface of the Earth. *Igneous* means *fire*. Basalt and olivine are types of igneous rocks. *Sedimentary rocks* are mixtures of rocks--such as gravel, mineral grains, and rock fragments--that have fused together by various processes. Shale, siltstone, and sandstone are sedimentary rocks. *Metamorphic rocks* have been subjected to pressure or heat, which actually changes the structure of the rock. Slate and marble are metamorphic rocks.

Keywords and Pronunciation

Andriji Mohorovicic (ahn-DREE-yah maw-hawr-oh-VEE-chech)

crust : Earth's hard, rocky covering. The crust is the outermost layer of the Earth.

crystal : A solid substance whose atoms are arranged in repeating patterns. Crystals can be very beautiful, often looking like jewels.

galena (guh-LEE-nuh)

igneous (IG-nee-uhs) : A class of rocks that forms from magma and lava. Obsidian may look like black glass but, in fact, it is a kind of igneous rock.

inner core : The center of Earth. Scientists think it is made of solid iron and nickel. The inner core has 30 times more mass than the moon.

mantle : the part of earth that is beneath the crust and is made up of rock; about 84 percent of the earth´s volume is in the mantle

metamorphic (meh-tuh-MOR-fik) : A class of rocks that forms when heat and pressure act on igneous or sedimentary rock.

mineral : A nonliving substance that is made up of crystals and is found in nature. The Earth´s crust contains many minerals.

outer core : The part of Earth that is beneath the mantle and contains melted iron and nickel. The outer core surrounds the inner core.

rock : A hard material made up of two or more minerals. There are three categories of rocks in the Earth.

TEACH
Activity 1: The Stuff of the Earth (Online)
Instructions

Have your student read through the Explore on her own. Reinforce and explain difficult concepts as needed.

Explore Suggestions:

Screen 1:

Cut an apple in half and compare it to the structure of the Earth. (The skin is the crust, the fruit of the apple is the mantle, and the pitted core is the core.)

After this activity, check to see if your student can do the following:

[A] Identify the four main layers of the Earth and describe their characteristics.

[B] Explain that rock is composed of different combinations of minerals.

If your student has difficulty with any of these concepts, you may wish to review the Explore with her and have her explain the key points on each screen.

Activity 2: Rock Sampling (Offline)
Instructions

This is the first time your student will see the rock kit. For these first few lessons she should not know the identity of the different rocks and minerals. If you have not already done so, remove the lid with the key from the box, and set it aside for later reference.

At the beginning of this activity, give your student time to explore each item in the kit. Encourage her to use the magnifying glass to take a look at each rock and mineral more closely. She will be asked to observe the color of each sample, as well as if she can see any crystals or different minerals throughout it. She may not be able to find visible crystals, even though the sample contains them.

ASSESS

Lesson Assessment: Rocks and Minerals (*Offline*)

Students will complete an offline assessment based on the lesson objectives. Print the assessment and have students complete it on their own. Use the answer key to score the assessment, and then enter the results online. The attached answer key is the most current and may not coincide with previously printed guides.

TEACH

Activity 3. Optional: Nearby Rocks (*Online*)

Name _____   Date _____

Rocks and Minerals Assessment Answer Key

Use the words in the Word Bank to label the different layers of the Earth and to fill in the blanks. You may use some words more than once or not at all.

Word Bank

mantle

crust

iron

inner core

outer core

minerals

rocks

nickel

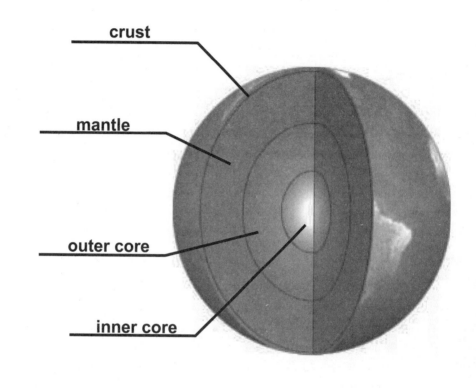

crust

mantle

outer core

inner core

1. The thin, hard, rocky outer layer is called the _____**crust**_____ .

2. The extremely hot layer that is made almost entirely of solid iron is the _____**inner core**_____ .

3. _____**Rocks**_____ are made up of two or more _____**minerals**_____ .

4. The _____**mantle**_____ is between the outer core and the crust. It is made of solid rock, but is under so much pressure that it is constantly moving.

5. The _____**outer core**_____ is made mostly of liquid iron.

Learning Coach Guide
Lesson 2: Crystal Shapes

Crystals, such as emeralds or rubies, are geological structures of the most beautiful kind. Their regular shapes and bright, sparkling colors have a scientific basis in the lattices that make them up.

Lesson Objectives

- Describe two types of crystal structures--cubic and hexagonal.
- Explain that the size of a crystal depends on the rate at which it was cooled.

PREPARE

Approximate lesson time is 60 minutes.

Advance Preparation

- In this science lesson, your student will be using the rock kit for the second time. For the first few lessons in this unit, we don't want her to know the identity of the different rocks and minerals. Remove the lid with the key from the box, and set it aside for later reference.
- Your student will need at least four days for crystals to grow in the "Cool" Crystals activity. Start the investigation early, or start it during the lesson and return to it later.

Materials

For the Student

- Crystal Shapes
- "Cool" Crystals

    jar - baby food/plastic cups (2)

    oven mitt

    salt - Epsom

    heat source

    magnifying glass

    pipe cleaners

    pot

    ruler

    safety goggles

    spoon

    water

Lesson Notes

Crystals have a distinctive shape and a special way of forming that are unlike any others in nature. If you look closely at a crystal you will see it has a regular, orderly shape. It has flat faces, called *plane surfaces*, which meet to form sharp angles. Crystals tend to reflect light well. Underneath their surfaces, crystals also have other things in common. They are made of one element, one compound, or a very regular mixture of compounds. The atoms or molecules that make up crystals all have a regular and repeating structure.

How Crystals Develop

When crystals grow, their atoms or molecules join together in special ways. Very specific conditions must be present for a crystal to develop. Crystals must have a free and unrestricted space in which to grow. The temperature also affects how fast crystals grow, and determines whether small or large crystals will form. A ruby crystal, for example, usually starts out as part of molten rock. As the rock cools, aluminum oxides settle out and begin to harden. If no other rocks or minerals are in the way, a ruby of almost pure aluminum oxide will form, and it will develop a regular shape as it grows. A touch of the element *chromium* gives the crystal its ruby-red color. If the rock cools very quickly, small crystals will form. If it cools slowly, larger crystals will form.

Shapes of Crystals

Crystals form in shapes that have a repeating pattern, called a *lattice*. The atoms and molecules in all crystals have some kind of lattice arrangement. When atoms or compounds are arranged in a lattice, the chemical organization of the substance is very regular and has a pattern. That is why many crystals have a regular shape. Scientists have identified fourteen different kinds of lattices, but each kind of crystal usually has only one type of lattice arrangement.

One arrangement is called a *cubic lattice*, in which the *cube* is the basic unit. The atoms, or a compound of the substance that makes up the crystal, will form as cubes stacked on top of each other and next to each other. Examples of crystals that form in a cubic lattice are silver, gold, diamonds, and rock salt. Another lattice pattern is a *hexagonal lattice*, in which the basic unit of the lattice is a *hexagon*. Examples of crystals whose atoms or compounds are arranged in a hexagonal lattice are ice, emeralds, and quartz.

There are many flat surfaces, or *planes*, within crystal lattices. When two planes meet, the result is an *edge*. This edge is actually caused by the arrangement of groups of molecules in the crystal. The planes and angles of crystals reflect light very well. If you shine a light on a crystal it will reflect off the flat surfaces in much the same way that it bounces off a mirror.

Common Uses of Crystals

Aside from being used in jewelry and decorations, crystals are a part of our everyday lives in many ways. Diamonds are the hardest of all naturally occurring substances. Tool manufacturers sometimes place diamonds on the tips of saw blades and drill bits to create a very sharp and long-lasting cutting edge. They put diamonds and similar jewels inside special machine parts to help prevent wear and tear. Crystals are also an important part of many watches. A certain kind of quartz crystal vibrates at an extremely regular and accurate rate. When this crystal is placed in a watch, it lets the watch tick off precise periods of time.

Keywords and Pronunciation

crystal : A substance, often made of a single compound or element, that forms in a regular repeating pattern as rocks cool. I found a quartz crystal inside a granite rock.

cubic : A type of crystal structure formed from stacks of four-sided shapes (cubes). The crystal structure of gold is cubic.

hexagonal : A type of crystal structure formed from six-sided shapes. Ice has a hexagonal crystal structure.

TEACH
Activity 1: Amazing Crystals (Online)
Instructions
Have your student read through the Explore on his own. Reinforce and explain difficult concepts as needed.

Explore Suggestions:

Check your student's understanding by asking the following questions:

- What makes crystals different from any other substance in nature? (their shapes and ways in which they form)
- What might affect the way a crystal grows? (space and temperature)
- Name two types of crystal patterns. (cubic and hexagonal)
- Name two uses for crystals. (in tools such as drills, in machines to prevent wear, in jewelry, and in watches to help keep time)

After this activity, check to see if your student can do the following:

- Describe two types of crystal structures--cubic and hexagonal.
- Explain that the size of a crystal depends on the rate at which it cooled.

If your student has difficulty with any of these concepts, you may wish to review the Explore with him and have him explain the key points on each screen.

Activity 2: Crystal Shapes (Offline)
Instructions
Teaching:

When crystals grow, their atoms or molecules join together in orderly ways. A crystal's specific type of repeating pattern is called a *lattice*. A *cubic lattice* is a pattern of stacked cubes. A *hexagonal lattice* is a pattern of stacked hexagons.

Troubleshooting:

Your student may have trouble identifying the crystal structure of the rocks from her kit. This is fine. Encourage her to observe closely before predicting.

What to Expect:

Your student should be able to identify and describe two types of crystal structures by the patterns of their lattices.

Answers:

A cubic lattice is formed from stacked **cubes**.

A hexagonal lattice is formed from stacked **hexagons**.

Observations:

1. Yes, all faces should be facing outward.

2. Rock 7 and Rock 10--hexagonal; Rock 14--cubic

Activity 3: "Cool" Crystals (*Offline*)
Instructions
Teaching:

One factor related to crystal size is how fast molten rock is cooled. Crystals that are formed in warm conditions cool slowly. Crystals formed in cold conditions cool quickly. Make sure your student understands this before beginning the activity.

Plastic cups may be substituted for jars.

What to Expect:

The crystals that formed in the refrigerator will be smaller than those that formed at room temperature. Your student should understand the relationship between the rate of cooling and the size of crystals.

Answers:

Check your student's hypothesis:

Is it a prediction? (yes)

Does it include the words *I think*? (no)

Analyze

1. Refrigerated jar--fastest, Room temperature jar--slowest

2. Refrigerated jar--smallest, Room temperature jar--largest

Conclusion

Crystals that cool slowly grow larger than those that cool quickly.

Safety

Perform this activity with an adult. Wear safety goggles and use caution when handling hot objects.

ASSESS

Lesson Assessment: Crystal Shapes (*Offline*)

Students will complete an offline assessment based on the lesson objectives. Print the assessment and have students complete it on their own. Use the answer key to score the assessment, and then enter the results online. The attached answer key is the most current and may not coincide with previously printed guides.

Name _____ Date _____

Lesson Assessment Answer Key

Circle the letter of the word that completes the sentence.

1. The special shapes in crystals show a pattern called a _____.
   a. hexagon
   b. cube
   (c.) lattice
   d. mineral

2. Label the crystal shapes with the name of their type of pattern.

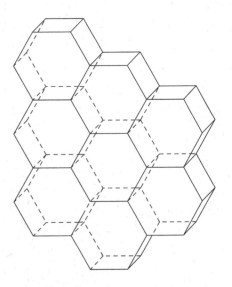

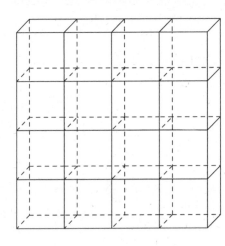

hexagonal _____

cubic _____

3. Some crystals are formed quickly when volcanic rock cools. How would those crystals compare to rock crystals that are formed over hundreds of years, deep in the Earth? Why? _____
   Those crystals would be smaller than the crystals that formed
   over hundreds of years. Rocks that cool quickly have smaller
   crystals.

Learning Coach Guide
Lesson 3: Properties of Minerals

In this lesson, your student will build his knowledge beyond the atomic structure of crystals. He will explore the world of crystalline compositions we call *minerals*. Your student will learn about the properties of minerals and how those properties can be used to identify the particular minerals that make up the rocks on Earth.

Lesson Objectives

- Recognize that you can identify minerals by their color, luster, hardness, streak, and specific gravity.

PREPARE

Approximate lesson time is 60 minutes.

Advance Preparation

- In this science lesson, your student will be using the rock kit. For the first few lessons in this unit, we don't want her to know the identity of the different rocks and minerals. Remove the lid with the key from the box, and set it aside for later reference.
- A white, porcelain streak plate is included in K12's additional science materials. If you do not have the plate, you will need to purchase at a home improvement store. The plate is a 2 inch piece of white ceramic tile.

Materials

    For the Student

        📖 Mystery Information List

        📖 Mystery Minerals

        coin - penny

        household item - porcelain streak plate

        flashlight

        K12 Rocks and Minerals Kit

        nail, iron

        📖 Mineral Information List

        📖 Specific Gravity

        bowl - 2 liter

        spring scale

        string - 60 cm

        water

Lesson Notes

Geologists organize minerals by their chemical makeup. Some of the most common types of minerals are listed below, but each of these types has many different variations. Even the same kind of mineral can have slight variations and slightly different properties.

Silicates: Composed mainly of silicon and oxygen. Examples include mica, feldspar, quartz, and olivine.

Carbonates: Composed mainly of calcium carbonate. Examples include calcite and dolomite.

Oxides: Composed of oxygen bound to metals. Examples include hematite and spinel.

Sulfur minerals: Contain the element sulfur. Examples include pyrite (fool's gold) and gypsum.

Methods of Identifying Minerals

Two of the most common ways geologists identify minerals are by looking at their chemical properties and by looking at their physical properties. This lesson covers five important physical properties of minerals.

Cleavage and Fracture - *Cleavage* describes how a mineral breaks along the planes of its lattice structure. If you strike mica with a hammer, for example, it cleaves into thin sheets. If you hit galena, it cleaves into cubes. Some minerals have irregular cleavage, which is called *fracture.*

Hardness - *Hardness* is a mineral's ability to withstand scratching. In 1822, an Austrian geologist named Friedrich Mohs developed a scale of mineral hardness that scientists still use today.

Luster - In addition to cleavage and hardness, scientists identify minerals by their *luster*--the way light reflects off the surfaces. Types of mineral luster are adamantine (sparkle), silky, pearly, greasy, resinous, vitreous (glassy), and metallic.

Color - Geologists can often identify the substances present in a mineral by color. Chalk is white or grayish. Rose quartz is pink. Copper is evidenced by its blue color, although some copper compounds are "copper colored," or reddish brown. Sulfur compounds are usually yellow or black. The colors in gemstones are often the result of impurities. The green of an emerald is from chromium. Titanium makes sapphires blue.

Streak - Geologists also use a technique called *streak* to verify the color they see in a mineral. If you scratch a mineral on a piece of unglazed white porcelain, the color of the mark, or *streak*, is often different from the color of the mineral. Gold, for example, makes a gold streak, but the gold-colored mineral pyrite makes a black streak.

Density and Specific Gravity - A final way geologists identify minerals is by measuring density. If you hold a piece of heavy hematite in one hand and a similar size piece of talc in the other, you can tell that hematite is denser. Hematite's molecules are larger than talc's, and are packed more tightly.

Geologists use a measure called *specific gravity* (SG) to identify minerals. Sensitive instruments can measure specific gravity, but a simple method involves weighing the mineral in air and in water. When you subtract the weight in water from the weight in air, then divide the weight in air by the result, you get the specific gravity of the mineral. The formula for determining specific gravity is $SG = X/X-Y$.

Keywords and Pronunciation

dolomite (DOH-luh-miyt)

galena (guh-LEE-nuh)

Hematite (HEE-muh-tiyt)

luster : The way light reflects off the surface of a mineral, or its shine. A silver coin has a metallic luster.

mica (MIY-kuh)

olivine (AH-luh-veen)

pyrite (PIY-riyt)

spinel (spuh-NEL)

TEACH
Activity 1: Qualities of Minerals *(Online)*
Instructions
Have your student read through the Explore on his own. Reinforce and explain difficult concepts as needed.

Explore Suggestions:

Check your student's understanding by asking the following questions:

1. What is the difference between a rock and a mineral? (Rocks are made of a mixture of minerals.)
2. List five tests that can be used to identify a mineral. (color, luster, hardness, streak, specific gravity)
3. What is wrong with labeling your rock kit a *Rock* Kit? (There are minerals in the kit, as well.)

After this activity, check to see if your student can do the following:

• Recognize that you can identify minerals by their color, luster, hardness, streak, and specific gravity.

If your student has difficulty with any of these concepts, you may wish to review the Explore with him and have him explain the key points on each screen.

Activity 2: Be a Geologist *(Offline)*
Instructions
Teaching:

Use this opportunity to reinforce the importance of scientific testing. The "friend" in the example uses a *subjective* test--one that's based on opinion--to identify the mineral. Scientists use *objective* tests--those that are based on mathematics and facts--to identify things. Of course, one test is not enough. Scientists know that they must repeat tests many times to make sure their data are reliable enough to make a decision. Review the tests for color, luster, hardness, and streak if necessary. Encourage your student to notice the specific gravity for the minerals he tests.

Troubleshooting:

Your student should be able to complete this activity independently. Assist him if he becomes overwhelmed with the amount of data collected. Check to see that he uses his notes to identify each mineral.

What to Expect:

Your student should be able to perform tests for mineral color, luster, hardness, and streak, and then identify minerals based on these tests.

Answers:

Mineral names

10 - Quartz

11 - Calcite

12 - Halite

13 - Fluorite

14 - Pyrite

15 - Talc

Conclusion

1. Minerals have their own properties. They differ in color, luster, hardness, streak, and specific gravity.

2. Organizing things into groups makes it easier to study them. When scientists find a new substance they are able to figure out what it is quickly by comparing it to other groups to spot ways in which they are alike.

3. Scientists repeat their tests to get them right.

Safety
As usual, you may wish to preview any books or websites listed in this lesson.

Activity 3. Optional: Specific Gravity (Offline)

Instructions

Teaching:

Specific gravity is another accurate test geologists use to identify minerals. It is based on a ratio of the mass of the mineral to the volume of water it displaces. Review water displacement with your student. She should understand that the amount of water displaced by an object is equal to the volume of that object. Refer back to the Forces in Fluids Unit for lessons on buoyancy and displacement if needed.

Troubleshooting:

It may be necessary to break your samples in order to fit them into the graduated cylinder. You may also need a more sensitive spring scale. Allow your student to use a calculator for difficult calculations.

What to Expect:

With assistance, your student should be able to accurately measure the specific gravity of the minerals in her K12 Rocks and Minerals Kit.

ASSESS

Lesson Assessment: Properties of Minerals (*Online*)

Review your student's responses on the Mystery Minerals activity and input the results online. The attached answer key is the most current and may not coincide with previously printed guides.

Lesson Assessment Answer Key

Properties of Minerals

Answers:

1. Mineral 10: ___quartz___
   Mineral 11: ___calcite___
   Mineral 12: ___halite___
   Mineral 13: ___fluorite___
   Mineral 14: ___pyrite___
   Mineral 15: ___talc___

Learning Coach Guide
Lesson 4: Mining of Minerals

Now that your student has learned something about minerals, let's pause in our examination of pure Earth science to look at some of the human needs for minerals. From diamonds for industrial saws to copper for electrical wires, people employ elements and minerals extensively. How are these substances taken from the Earth and prepared for industrial and other uses?

Lesson Objectives

- Define ore as rock with a high metal content.
- Describe the activity of producing aluminum from bauxite as an example of processing ore.
- Describe some of the everyday uses of minerals.

PREPARE

Approximate lesson time is 60 minutes.

Materials

For the Student

📖 Minerals All Around

📖 Minerals Around the World Map

household item - see Minerals All Around sheet

pencil

Lesson Notes

Minerals are a non-renewable natural resource--once we use them, we can recycle them but not return them easily into the form in which we got them. They must be mined from the ground and then processed to make them fit to use. Modern mineral-exploration methods may involve digging exploratory shafts and examining cores of material from the Earth. Geologists send seismic blasts into the ground and use radar to find out whether minerals are present. Metal miners try to detect certain ores with strong magnets. Mining removes minerals from the ground, but they are not pure minerals in most cases. Miners dig up chunks of rocks that contain large amounts of some specific mineral. Mineral-containing rock or earth is called *ore*. Once ore is removed from the ground, it is taken to a refinery where machines crush the ore and then separate out the needed minerals.

Methods of Mining

There are many ways to get minerals out of the ground, including surface mining, underground mining, placer mining, and underwater mining.

Surface Mining--One of the most common methods is *surface mining*, in which the surface layer of earth is removed down to the layers that contain minerals. Explosives blast loose the mineral-bearing earth, then machines remove the ore. The mining continues until the area contains no more ore. Geologists call this method *open-pit mining*. When the earth contains coal, the mining process is called *strip-mining*. Open-pit mining and strip-mining cause a lot of damage to the environment. Modern mining operations are trying to reduce the damage by using a process called *opencasting*, in which machines return much of the rock and soil to the pit. Workers then plant trees and seed to help nature reclaim the land.

Underground Mining--Ores often occur in underground *veins*--distinct areas that contain a great deal of a specific kind of ore. To get to a vein, miners dig holes and passageways in the ground. Such mines are called *underground mines*. Many old-time gold and silver mines in the western United States were underground mines.

Placer Mining--Erosion or the shifting of earth may expose gravelly rock, called *talus*, on hillsides or stream banks. Talus and the rock under it may be high in minerals. In this case, a process called *placer mining* removes the ore.

Underwater Mining--The ocean floor is a vast reservoir of minerals but, as yet, very few underwater mining ventures have made money. In the 1950s, an American named Sam Collins decided to mine diamonds from the bottom of the ocean. His company, Tidal Diamonds, mined the sea off the coast of Namibia in southern Africa. Scooping earth from the ocean floor, Tidal Diamonds collected 1.5 million carats (300 kg or 661 pounds) of diamonds. In the future we may see more efforts to gather minerals from the ocean floor.

Keywords and Pronunciation

ore : Rock with a high metal content. Bingham Canyon Mine processes a great deal of copper ore.
surface mining : A form of mining that strips off the surface layer of earth and digs down to the mineral-containing layers. Huge explosions at the surface-mining site lifted layers off of the ground for the miners.
talus (TAY-luhs)

TEACH
Activity 1: Metals from the Earth *(Online)*
Instructions
Have your student read through the Explore on her own. Reinforce and explain difficult concepts as needed.
Explore Suggestions:
Screen 1: Review the difference between a renewable and non-renewable resource with your student. A renewable resource is one that can be replaced in its original form. A non-renewable resource is a resource that is used up faster than it can be produced.
Screen 5: Ask your student to describe the steps by which bauxite is processed, in order. If she is not able to, review this screen again.
After this activity, check to see if your student can:
- Define *ore* as rock with a high metal content.
- Describe the procedure by which aluminum is produced from bauxite as an example of processing ore.
- Describe some of the everyday uses of minerals.

If your student has difficulty with any of these concepts, you may wish to review the Explore with her and have her explain the key points on each screen.

Activity 2: If It Can't be Grown, It Has to Be Mined (Offline)

Instructions

Teaching:

Minerals make up almost everything that we use each day to make our lives more comfortable. Your student will be asked to look at her surroundings and make a list of the things that she thinks come from minerals. She will then look for the items on the provided chart to see which minerals they contain.

Your student will then be asked to pick two of the items from the list. Using the Minerals All Around chart and Minerals Around the World map, she will find where the minerals are mined. Using a key that she develops, she will mark the country where each mineral can be found.

Your student will also be asked to describe the process by which bauxite is turned into aluminum.

Troubleshooting:

You may need to help your student make the key to her World map. Suggest that she use symbols such as triangles and stars to represent each mineral. Be sure that she is consistent when showing where the same mineral is mined in different parts of the world.

If needed, allow your student to look back at the Explore section that describes the steps in processing bauxite. Adjust based on activity.

Answers:

1. skateboard: contains iron (mined in Russia and China)

2. fruit juice: contains perlite (mined in U.S. and Greece) and diatomite (mined in the U.S., France, and Romania)

3. pencil: contains graphite (mined in Korea and India) and clay (mined in the U.S.)

4. soda can: contains aluminum (mined in Australia and Guinea)

ASSESS

Lesson Assessment: Mining of Minerals (*Offline*)

Students will complete an offline assessment based on the lesson objectives. Print the assessment and have students complete it on their own. Use the answer key to score the assessment, and then enter the results online. The attached answer key is the most current and may not coincide with previously printed guides.

TEACH

Activity 3: Visit the Mineral Information Institute (Online)

Instructions

Visit the Mineral Information Institute with your student. There is information about how mining affects the environment, as well as many activities that you and your young geologist can do.

Safety

As usual, you may wish to preview any books or websites listed in this lesson.

Name _____   Date _____

Minerals All Around

Almost all of the things we use every day are made from minerals. All the items you use at home, at play, to do work, and even some things we eat come from minerals that are mined from the Earth.

Look around your house for the following objects. Observe the objects and predict what minerals might be in them. Then, look them up on the chart called Minerals All Around. Were you surprised?

Minerals can be found in countries all around the world. Some countries, such as the U.S. and Russia, have many different minerals mined from them. Where do all of the minerals come from that make up the paper this is written on, or the pencil you are using? Use the Where in the World chart to record the countries where the minerals can be found.

Common household items	Minerals I predict may be in them	Minerals actually in them	Where they are mined
drinking glass			
fruit juice			
pencil			
soda can			

How could a friend who doesn't know much about minerals see where they come from? A map! You now have all the information you need to show where in the world these minerals come from. Think of a symbol, such as a triangle or star, for each mineral in your table. Use these symbols to show what countries they are mined in on the world map. Be sure to create a key so that your friend can read your map.

Name _____ Date _____

Minerals All Around

Baby Powder: Talc
Batteries: Antimony, Cadmium, Lead, Zinc
Bicycle: Aluminum, Clay, Diatomite, Mica Sulfur, Selenium, Wollastonite, Zinc
Books: Clay, Limestone, Sodium Sulfate, Feldspar
Bricks: Bauxite, Chromite, Zircon, Silica, Graphite, Kyanite, Andalusite, Sillimanite, Clays
Cake/Bread: Gypsum, Phosphates
Car: Platinum, Iron, Aluminum, Lead, Coal, Barite, Boron, Calcium Carbonate, Bentonite, Silica, Chromium, Perlite, Wollastonite, Mica, Industrial Diamonds, Zeolite, Clays
Carpet: Calcium Carbonate, Limestone
Clothing: Boron, Halite, Molybdenum, Sulfur
Desk: Copper, Iron, Zinc, Nickel
Digital Alarm Clock: Boron, Copper, Gold, Quartz
Drinking Glass: Boron, Silica
Drinking Water: Limestone, Lime, Salt, Fluorite
Fruit Juice: Perlite, Diatomite
Glass/Ceramics: Silica sand, Limestone, Talc, Lithium, Borates, Soda Ash, Feldspar
Ink: Calcium Carbonate
Lights: Aluminum, Copper, Beryllium (fluorescent), Tungsten (incandescent), Tin, Nickel
Linoleum: Calcium Carbonate, Clay, Wollastonite
Kitty Litter: Attapulgite, Montmorillonite, Zeolites, Diatomite, Pumice, Volcanic Ash

Paint: Titanium Oxide, Clays, Limestone, Mica, Talc, Silica, Copper, Fluorspar, Iron, Tungsten, Zinc, Cadmium
Paper: Boron, Clay, Kaolin, Sulfur, Talc, Titanium, Trona
Pencils: Graphite, Clay
Pencil Sharpener: Iron, Copper, Zinc
Plastic: Limestone, Wollastonite, Coal, Talc, Silica, Petroleum Products
Pots and Pans: Aluminum, Iron, copper
Potting Soil: Titanium Dioxide, Kaolin Clays, Calcium Carbonate, Mica, Talc, Silica, Wollastonite
Skateboard: Aluminum, Calcium Carbonate, Clay, Coal, Iron, Mica, Sulfur, Silica, Talc, Wollastonite
Soda Can: Aluminum
Sports Equipment: Graphite, Fiberglass
Telephone: Aluminum, Beryllium, Coal, Copper, Gold, Iron, Limestone, Silica, Silver, Talc, Wollastonite
Television set: Aluminum, Antimony, Barite, Beryllium, Cobalt, Columbium, Copper, Europium, Gallium, Germanium, Gold, Indium, Iron, Kaolin, Lanthanides, Limestone, Lithium, Manganese, Mercury, Mica, Molybdenum, Platinum, Rhenium, Selenium, Silica, Strontium, Tantalum, Tellurium, Terbium, Tin, Titanium, Vanadium, Yttrium, Zinc, Zirconium
Toothpaste: Calcium Carbonate, Limestone, Sodium Carbonate, Fluorite
Wallpaper: Mica, Trona

Name _____ Date _____

Minerals All Around: Where in the World

Aluminum (Bauxite)	Australia, Guinea
Andalusite	South Africa, India
Barite	China, India
Beryllium	U.S., Russia
Borates	Turkey, U.S.
Cadmium	Japan, Belgium
Chromite	South Africa, Russia
Clays	U.S.
Copper	Chile, U.S.
Diatomite	U.S., France, Romania
Feldspar	Italy, U.S.
Fluorspar	China, Mongolia
Graphite	Korea, India
Gravel	U.S.
Gypsum	U.S., Canada
Industrial Diamonds	Australia, Zaire
Iron	Russia, China
Kyanite	SouthAfrica, India, France
Lead	Australia, U.S.
Lime	Russia, China
Limestone	U.S.
Micas	U.S., Russia
Nickel	Russia, Canada
Perlite	U.S., Greece
Platinum	South Africa, Russia
Potash	Russia, Canada
Pumice	Italy, Greece
Selenium	Japan, Canada
Silica Sand	U.S., Netherlands
Sillimanite	South Africa
Sodium Sulfate	Mexico, Spain
Sulfur	U.S., Russia
Talc	Japan, U.S.
Tin	China, Brazil
Titanium	Russia, Japan
Trona (Soda Ash)	U.S., Kenya
Tungsten	China, Russia
Vermiculite	South Africa, U.S.
Wollastonite	Germany, Great Britain
Zeolites	U.S., Tanzania
Zinc	Canada, Australia
Zircon	Australia, South Africa

Name _____   Date _____

Mining of Minerals Assessment Answer Key

1. Rock that contains minerals and has a high metal content is called
   _____ **ore** _____ .

2. We use minerals in our everyday lives. Name one mineral you use
   every day. _____
   Tell what the mineral is used in. _____
   Answers will vary but should include items and information

   from the chart on the attached *Minerals all Around* PDF.

   _____

3. Bauxite is an ore that contains many minerals including aluminum.
   Put the steps involved in processing bauxite in order by writing the
   numbers 1-4 in the blanks below.

   4___ The melted aluminum metal is poured into molds to cool.

   2___ Machines at a refinery crush the ore, clean it, and heat it
   to produce a pure chemical high in the element aluminum.

   1___ Open-pit mining removes bauxite from the ground.

   3___ A hot furnace called a *smelter* purifies the aluminum.

Learning Coach Guide
Lesson 5: The Rock Cycle

The rock cycle, in which igneous, sedimentary, and metamorphic rock are destroyed and reformed, takes place over vast stretches of time. By understanding the rock cycle, your student will be able to understand rocks not as unchanging objects, but as part of a great recycling process for the minerals of our active planet, Earth.

Lesson Objectives

- Identify the three different types of rocks and how they form.
- Describe what is meant by the term *rock cycle.*

PREPARE

Approximate lesson time is 60 minutes.

Materials

For the Student

      Rock Formation

      K12 Rocks and Minerals Kit

      Rock Recipes

      pencil

      butter - 75 g (2 1/2 tbls.)

      chocolate chips - 75 g (1/2 cup)

      egg

      flour - 150 g (1 cup + 2 tbls.)

      household item - vanilla (1/2 tsp.)

      measuring spoon

      sugar - 125 g (2/3 cup)

      bowl - large mixing

      cookie sheet - greased

      measuring cup

      spoon

For the Adult

      Rock Formation Answer Key

Lesson Notes

Over long periods of time, processes within the Earth build up rocks and break them down again. By studying rocks, geologists have been able to piece together some of the most important events in our planet's immensely long history. Rocks are all different because of the minerals they contain, and also because they cooled at different rates as they formed. By studying the minerals in a rock and the size of the mineral crystals, you can get a good idea of how the rock formed. Geologists have determined that there are three main kinds of rocks: igneous, metamorphic, and sedimentary. They have also determined that these rock types are related.

Igneous Rock

Igneous means *formed by fire*. Igneous rocks form wherever *magma*--molten rock in the Earth's mantle-- pushes through the crust. Magma that reaches the surface or pushes up through the bottom of the ocean is called *lava*. As magma and lava cool down, minerals within them crystallize, and rocks form.

Sedimentary Rock

Sediments are finely divided layers of rock and mud that form at the bottom of lakes, streams, rivers, and oceans. Sediment forms when running water, wind, or waves break up rocks. The debris washes away and gets deposited in land or water as rubble. Over time, some of the rock bits in the rubble cement together to form new rocks. These build up as layers, are compacted by pressure, and finally cement together to form new rocks. Most of the rocks we see aboveground are sedimentary rocks. As with igneous rocks, geologists study the mineral content of sedimentary rocks to find out their origin. They also get clues from the size of the rock particles, and by studying how the rocks are cemented together.

Metamorphic Rock

The word *metamorphosis* comes from a Greek word that means *to change shape*. *Metamorphic rocks* form when rocks are subjected to large amounts of pressure, heat, or chemical reactions. Small amounts of pressure or heat can also produce metamorphic rocks, but these rocks change only slightly and may look quite a bit like the original rocks. Other times, huge amounts of pressure or heat or the presence of certain chemicals can completely change the rocks, even altering their minerals.

The Rock Cycle

The *rock cycle* is a series of processes in which one kind of rock is transformed into other kinds. The rock cycle takes place all over the Earth. Each step in the process may take millions of years. In the cycle, each type of rock can change into the other two types of rock.

Keywords and Pronunciation

gneiss (niys)

igneous (IG-nee-uhs) : A class of rocks that forms from magma and lava. Obsidian may look like black glass but, in fact, it is a kind of igneous rock.

metamorphic (meh-tuh-MOR-fik) : A class of rocks that forms when heat and pressure act on igneous or sedimentary rock.

metamorphosis (meh-tuh-MOR-fuh-suhs) : the process of change in the shape or composition of rocks, caused by heat, pressure, or chemical reactions acting over time

rock cycle : The pathways by which rocks change from one form to another over time. Igneous rocks and metamorphic rocks are part of the rock cycle.

sediment : Layers of rock and mud that form at the bottom of lakes, streams, rivers, and oceans. The sediment at the bottom of the bay is mostly mud.

sedimentary : Rocks that form when other rocks layer and fuse with each other. Sandstone is a kind of sedimentary rock.

TEACH
Activity 1: Ever-Changing Rocks (Online)
Instructions

Have your student read through the Explore on her own. Reinforce and explain difficult concepts as needed. *After this activity, check to see if your student can do the following:*

- Identify the three different types of rocks and how they form.
- Describe what is meant by the term *rock cycle*.

If your student has difficulty with any of these concepts, you may wish to review the Explore with her and have her explain the key points on each screen.

Safety

As usual, you may wish to preview any books or websites listed in this lesson.

Activity 2: Rock Formation (Offline)
Instructions

Teaching:

Your student will use some of the sedimentary, metamorphic, and igneous rocks in her rock kit. She will be asked to identify the different types of rock and rock names based on their description and to label where they are formed on the Rock Formation sheet.

Troubleshooting:

If your student is having difficulty remembering where each type of rock is formed, have her review the Explore section.

Your student may wish to write more recipe cards about some of the specific rocks from their rock kit such as for gneiss or basalt. Have her visit one of the following websites to gather the information she will need to create her recipes.

Rocks, Minerals and Soils Introduction

Rocks and Minerals Slide Show

Rock Hounds

Activity 3: Rock Recipes (Online)
Instructions

Teaching:

In this activity, your student will be asked to write some rock "recipes." The ingredients will be things such as sediment particles, heat, and pressure. She will be provided with a recipe for igneous rocks as an example. Let your student be creative with her recipes. The answers provided are just examples of some of the components she should use. Before your student starts the activity, review the different components needed to form each type of rock.

Troubleshooting:

If your student is having difficulty writing her recipes, have her think about how each type of rock forms differently from the other two types. Some ingredients may be the same for the sedimentary, metamorphic, and igneous rocks.

What to Expect:

Answers:

These are only examples of possible recipes--let your student be creative.

Sedimentary Rock Recipe

1 part igneous or metamorphic rock from a lake, stream, river, or ocean

1,000 waves to break up the rocks into sediment

5 parts pressure to cement the sediment particles together to form sedimentary rock

Metamorphic Rock Recipe

1 part igneous or sedimentary rock

500 parts extreme pressure

500 parts extreme heat

Mix the three ingredients together to form metamorphic rock.

Extension:

Your student may wish to write more recipe cards about some of the specific rocks from her rock kit, such as gneiss or basalt. Have her visit one of the following websites to gather the information she will need to create her recipes.

Rocks, Minerals, and Soils Introduction

Rocks and Minerals Slide Show

Rock Hounds

Sedimentary Rock Textures

ASSESS

Lesson Assessment: The Rock Cycle (*Offline*)

Students will complete an offline assessment based on the lesson objectives. Print the assessment and have students complete it on their own. Use the answer key to score the assessment, and then enter the results online. The attached answer key is the most current and may not coincide with previously printed guides.

TEACH

Activity 4. Optional: Metamorphic Rock Cookies (*Offline*)

Instructions

Help your student make a batch of Metamorphic Chocolate Chip Cookies. When they are finished baking, discuss how they are like metamorphic rocks. The ingredients for chocolate chip cookies are something like the minerals in metamorphic rock--when you heat the mixture, it changes it into something else. Then sit back and enjoy your metamorphic treat.

Safety

This lesson involves eating or working with food. Before beginning, check with your doctor, if necessary, to find out whether your student will have any allergic reaction to the food.

Name _____   Date _____

Rock Formation Answer Key

Many of the samples in your rock kit are examples of sedimentary, metamorphic or igneous rock. Take the pumice, basalt, limestone, sandstone, marble and gneiss samples out of the kit.

Match each item on the left to its correct description on the right.

igneous rock ○

pumice ○

basalt ○

metamorphic rock ○

marble ○

gneiss ○

sedimentary rock ○

limestone ○

sandstone ○

○ A class of rocks formed when heat and pressure act on igneous or sedimentary rock. Marble, which is an example of this kind of rock, forms under great pressure.

○ This metamorphic rock is dark but looks like it has stripes of minerals running through it. The visible crystals make it shimmer.

○ This rock is formed by cooled lava filed with gas bubbles. It is white or light gray and might look like a rock froth.

○ Layers may be visible in this reddish-brown sedimentary rock.

○ Rocks that form when other rocks are cemented together. Sandstone is an example of this kind of rock.

○ This metamorphic rock is white and sparkles with crystals that are easy to see.

○ A class of rocks formed from magma and lava.

○ This rock is volcanic rock, so it is igneous. It is dark gray and very hard. You may see holes in it made by gas bubbles.

○ This whitish-gray sedimentary rock is powdery, with few visible crystals.

Rock Formation Answer Key

Study the picture below. Use the words from the Word Bank to correctly label the picture.

Word Bank

| igneous rock | metamorphic rock | sedimentary rock |

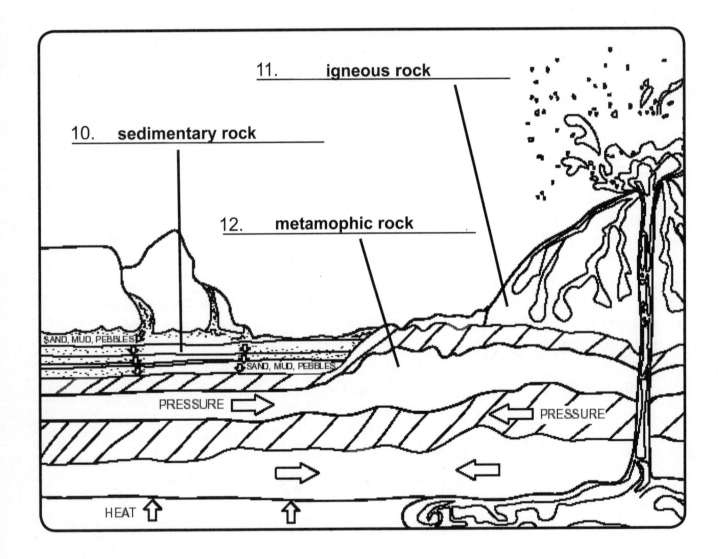

11. **igneous rock**

10. **sedimentary rock**

12. **metamophic rock**

SAND, MUD, PEBBLES

SAND, MUD, PEBBLES

PRESSURE

PRESSURE

HEAT

Name _____   Date _____

The Rock Cycle Assessment Answer Key

1. Which of the following best describes the rock cycle?
   A. The rock cycle is a process in which pressure causes sediment particles to cement together.
   B. The rock cycle is a series of processes in which one kind of rock is transformed into other kinds.
   C. The rock cycle is a series of processes in which water, wind, or waves break up rocks.
   D. The rock cycle is a process in which heated magma cools to form igneous rock.

2. Write the word *metamorphic*, *sedimentary,* or *igneous* in front of the statement that best describes how each is formed.

   sedimentary These rocks form when bits of rock are compacted by pressure and cement together to form new rocks.

   metamorphic These rocks form when other rocks are subjected to large amounts of pressure, heat, or chemical reactions.

   igneous These rocks form in volcanoes and wherever magma pushes through the Earth's crust.

The Rock Cycle Assessment Answer Key

3. Label the different parts of the rock cycle where igneous, sedimentary, and metamorphic rock are formed.

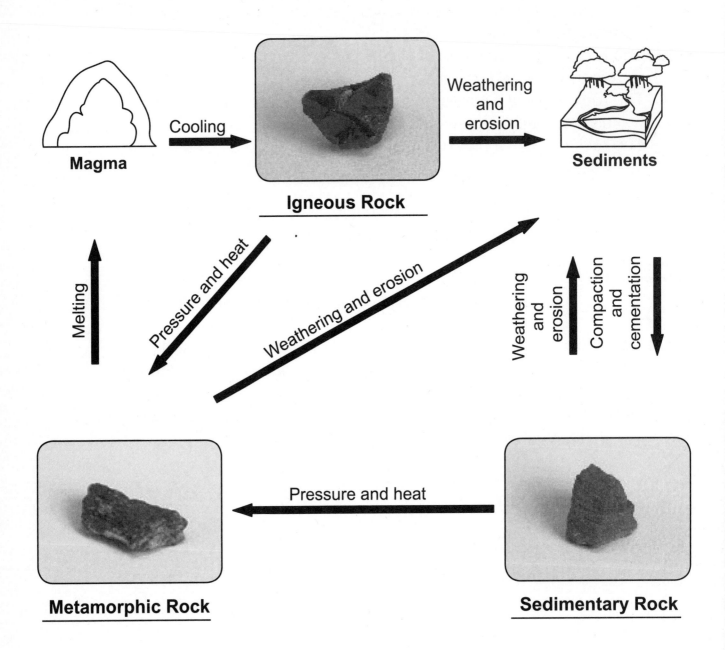

Learning Coach Guide
Lesson 6: Drifting Continents

Scientific evidence clearly shows that the continents have moved relative to one another. This phenomenon is known as *continental drift* and explains many biological and geological discoveries. Perhaps no geological theory is more surprising, and exciting, than continental drift.

Lesson Objectives

- Describe Alfred Wegener's theory of continental drift.
- Explain that earth's crust is made up of rigid plates that are always moving.
- Describe three types of plate boundaries.

PREPARE

Approximate lesson time is 60 minutes.

Materials

For the Student

    Pangaea Puzzle

    paper, construction, 9" x 12"

    scissors

    Plate Boundaries

    pencil

    Mountain Models

    clay

    hairpins

    household item - roll of calculator paper

    tissue paper - two or three colors

    cardboard - sheet 12 x 20 inches

    ruler, metric

    tape, masking

For the Adult

    Plate Boundaries Answer Key

Lesson Notes

In 1915 a German scientist named Alfred Wegener came up with a startling hypothesis about the continents. He suggested that at some time in our planet's history, all the present continents were one enormous land mass. He called this giant landmass *Pangaea*. He also introduced the idea of *continental drift*, which suggests that the individual continents are not anchored permanently in place, but float over the earth's surface.

Evidence of Continental Drift

Dr. Wegener presented many pieces of evidence to support his hypothesis. One obvious piece of data is that the continents *look* like jigsaw-puzzle pieces. Wegener was the first to think that these interlocking shapes did not happen by accident. He also found that fossils of exactly the same type existed in West Africa and South America. Additionally, some of the plants and animals in Africa and North America turned out to be closely related. Mountain ranges in different continents lined up to make one long chain. Rock types matched from one continent to another. Continents that may have touched had similar climates in the past.

One of the main reasons scientists did not want to accept the idea of continental drift was that Wegener presented no evidence showing what force had caused the continents to move. But by the 1950s, though, scientists had collected so much evidence for continental drift that they began trying to find the answer. After many studies they determined that the earth's crust consists of about 20 rigid plates that float around slowly on the earth's mantle. They found that molten rock, or *magma*, emerges from the mantle at the area between the plates. Magma is very powerful when it moves, and it adds so much rock to the surface of the earth that it actually forces the plates to move. The theory that describes this process is called the *theory of plate tectonics*.

Divergent, Convergent, and Transform Boundaries

The edges of the plates--called *boundaries*--have different names depending on how they interact with other plates.

Divergent Boundary--At a divergent boundary, the edges of two plates are moving apart. One of the main places magma emerges from the earth's mantle is at *divergent boundaries*. As magma pours out it adds igneous rock to both plates. It also pushes the plates apart. This process occurs at the bottom of the oceans and is called *seafloor spreading*.

Convergent Boundary--At a convergent boundary, the edges of two plates are moving toward each other. When two continental plates collide, neither gives way. As the plates continue to push together, the land at the boundary becomes crumpled and rises up, forming mountains. When an oceanic plate collides with a continental plate, the oceanic plate forces its way under the continental plate. This is called *subduction*. All the rock in the oceanic plate is forced down so far into the hot magma that it melts. The crust is so unstable at this kind of convergent boundary that magma from below the crust may break through and erupt as a volcano.

Transform Boundary--At a transform boundary, the edges of two plates are sliding past each other. When two plates slide against each other in different directions, earthquakes may occur. Transform boundaries are often called *faults*.

As usual, you may wish to preview any books or websites listed in this lesson.

Keywords and Pronunciation

Alfred Wegener (AHL-frayt VAY-guh-nuhr)

Himalaya (hih-muh-LAY-uh)

oceanic (oh-shee-A-nihk)

Pangaea (pan-JEE-uh) : the name scientists give to a supercontinent that once existed on earth

San Andreas (san an-DRAY-uhs)

Theory of Plate Tectonics : the scientific theory that earth's crust is made up of about 20 huge plates that are always moving very slowly

TEACH
Activity 1: Pangaea Puzzle *(Offline)*
Instructions
Have your student explore how the pieces of land may have fit together to form Pangaea. The pieces will not match up exactly.

Activity 2: Movement of Continents *(Online)*
Instructions
Have your student read through the Explore on her own. Reinforce and explain difficult concepts as needed.

Explore Suggestions:

Screen 1: Have your student keep her Pangaea Puzzle next to her as she reads through the Explore section. If necessary, have her adjust her pieces to match the illustration onscreen.

Screen 4: Before moving on, be sure that your student can describe the three ways in which plates can interact with each other: their edges can move toward each other, move away from each other, or slide past each other.

Screen 5: Your student might get upset when she realizes that the continents are still drifting. Assure her that the plates have been moving so slowly during each year of her life that she hasn't even noticed it.

Screen 7: Ask your student to describe what the results may be as the edges of plates bump up against each other or when they slide against each other.

After this activity, check to see if your student can do the following:
- Describe Alfred Wegener's theory of continental drift.
- Explain that earth's crust is made up of rigid plates that are always moving.
- Describe three types of plate boundaries.

If your student has difficulty with any of these concepts, you may wish to review the Explore with her and have her explain the key points on each screen.

Activity 3: Plate Boundaries *(Offline)*
Instructions
Teaching:

In this activity, your student will review what happens when the edges of two plates move against each other. She will be asked to describe what is happening in each picture and what the results of the collision may be. Her answers on the activity sheet will be used in the lesson assessment.

Troubleshooting:

If needed, allow your student to go back and look at the last few screens of the Explore section to answer the questions.

What to Expect:

When an oceanic plate collides with a continent plate, the oceanic plate forces its way under the continental plate. The rocks that make up the oceanic plate are forced down so far that they melt. The crust is so unstable at this kind of boundary that magma may break through, causing a volcano to erupt.

When two continental plates collide against each other, they push until the land at the boundary becomes folded and rises up. As the plates continue to collide, the mountain grows bigger and bigger.

When two plates slide against each other in opposite directions, an earthquake may occur.

ASSESS
Lesson Assessment: Drifting Continents (*Online*)

Students will complete an offline assessment based on the lesson objectives. Print the assessment and have students complete it on their own. Use the answer key to score the assessment, and then enter the results online. The attached answer key is the most current and may not coincide with previously printed guides.

TEACH
Activity 4. Optional: Mountain Models (*Offline*)
Instructions

In this activity, your student will build a model to show what happens when two continental plates push against each other. The two clay blocks represent two moving plates. The tissue paper represents the sedimentary rock that becomes trapped between the plates. When the two blocks collide, they push the tissue paper up to create a "mountain."

Name _____ Date _____

Plate Boundaries Answer Key

Look at the pictures of the different plates moving against each other. Describe what is happening in each picture and what the results may be.

Description: When an oceanic plate collides with a continent plate, the oceanic plate forces its way under the continental plate. The rocks that make up the oceanic plate are forced down so far that they melt.

Results: The crust is so unstable at this kind of boundary that magma may break through the crust causing a volcano to erupt.

_____

Description: When two continental plates collide against each other, they push and push, until the land at the boundary becomes folded and rises up.

_____

Results: As the plates continue to collide, a mountain will form and grow bigger and bigger.

_____

_____

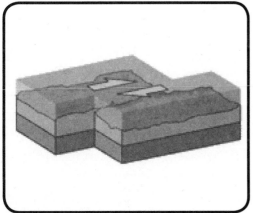

Description: Two plates are sliding against each other in opposite directions.

_____

_____

Results: When this takes place, an earthquake may occur.

_____

_____

Lesson Assessment Answer Key

Drifting Continents

Answers:

1. Answers may vary but should include: Alfred Wegener theorized that the continents were not anchored, but instead float over the Earth's surface. He believed the seven continents used to be connected to form the supercontinent Pangaea.

2. plates

3. When an oceanic plate collides with a continental plate, the oceanic plate forces its way under the continental plate. The rocks that make up the oceanic plate are forced down so they melt. The crust is so unstable at this kind of boundary that magma may break though the crust causing a volcano to erupt.

4. When two continental plates collide against each other, they push and push, until the land at the boundary becomes folded and rises up. As the plates continue to collide, a mountain will form and grow bigger and bigger.

5. When two plates are sliding against each other in opposite directions, an earthquake may occur.

Learning Coach Guide
Lesson 7: Volcanoes

Volcanoes are not only spectacular, they give us real insight into the deep, inner workings of the Earth. The images most people have of volcanoes are of huge, Fuji-like mountains on the verge of eruption. Yet there are many kinds of volcanoes, and each has its own unique properties.

Lesson Objectives

- Identify the main parts of a volcano: magma chamber, vent, and crater.
- Identify and describe the three types of land volcanoes (cinder cone, composite, and shield).
- Explain how volcanoes are formed.

PREPARE

Approximate lesson time is 60 minutes.

Materials

 For the Student
  🖥 Volcanoes
   pencil
 For the Adult
  🖥 Volcanoes Answer Key

Lesson Notes

How do volcanoes form and what makes them so spectacular? You can think of a volcano as an outlet for magma--molten rock within the Earth. Magma in the mantle is under great pressure. When it works it way through the crust and reaches the surface it is called *lava*.

Volcanoes are either active or extinct. An *extinct volcano* is one that no longer has the ability to erupt. Scientists sometimes have a hard time knowing when a volcano is extinct, because volcanoes can erupt with very little warning. An *active volcano* is one that has the ability to erupt, even though it may be quiet for long periods. Some quiet volcanoes still spew sulfur-filled gases, and may rumble and smoke from time to time.

We usually think of volcanoes as mountains, but volcanoes can also be cracks or fissures in the Earth's crust. Much of the mid-Atlantic ocean bottom has fissure volcanoes. Fissure volcanoes occur at plate boundaries where magma is forcing apart two oceanic plates. *Mountainous volcanoes* usually occur at places where one plate is sliding under another. As one massive plate moves down through the crust and into the mantle, the results can be dramatic. Magma pushes through the crust and spews out of the ground as lava.

There are three kinds of land volcanoes.

- *Cinder cone*--This is simply a small hill of cooled cinders and lava. Lava comes up out of the ground for a while and creates a cinder cone.
- *Shield volcano*--These form when lava flows out of a low volcanic hill over time. The lava may spread across land for quite a distance. The shield volcano Mauna Loa in Hawaii is only about 4 km above sea level. But measured from its true underwater base it is 10 km high--the tallest mountain on Earth. Its base under the sea is as big as Rhode Island. Shield volcanoes have gentle slopes.
- *Composite volcano*--These form from both lava flows and cinder rocks. These are the towering volcanoes, such as Mt. Fuji in Japan or Etna in Italy.

Keywords and Pronunciation

lava : magma that is extruded to the surface of the Earth´s crust

magma : Molten rock that is under the surface of the earth. The upper crust and lower mantle are places where magma is found.

Paricutin (pahr-REE-koo-teen)

volcano : Any areas of the Earth in which magma is extruded to the surface. Most volcanoes are situated at the edges of continental plates.

TEACH
Activity 1: The Fire from Below *(Online)*

Instructions

Have your student read through the Explore on her own. Reinforce and explain difficult concepts as needed.

Explore Suggestions:

Screen 2: Review the layers of the Earth with your student. Ask her to describe the characteristics of each layer.

Screen 3: Have your student describe each part of the volcano as she points to it on the screen.

Screen 4: Ask you student to explain the difference between an extinct and an active volcano.

Screen 5: Be sure your student can identify and describe the main parts of a volcano.

After this activity, check to see if your student can do the following:

- Identify the main parts of a volcano: magma chamber, vent, and crater.
- Identify and describe the three types of land volcanoes (cinder cone, composite, and shield).
- Explain how volcanoes are formed.

If your student has difficulty with any of these concepts, you may wish to review the Explore with her and have her explain the key points on each screen.

Safety

As usual, you may wish to preview any books or websites listed in this lesson.

Activity 2: Volcanoes *(Offline)*

Instructions

Teaching:

Your student will be asked to draw the different types of land volcanoes and describe how they formed. She will also be labeling the main parts of a volcano: the magma chamber, vent, and crater.

Troubleshooting:

If needed, allow your student to look back at the Explore section to complete this activity.

What to Expect:

See Answer Key for answers.

ASSESS

Lesson Assessment: Volcanoes (*Online*)

Students will complete an online assessment based on the lesson objectives. The assessment will be scored by the computer. The attached answer key is the most current and may not coincide with previously printed guides.

TEACH

Activity 3. Optional: Volcanoes Around the World (*Offline*)

Instructions

Visit Volcano World to discover volcanoes in countries all around the world.

Name _____ Date _____

Volcanoes Answer Key

You have learned about three types of land volcanoes: cinder cone, shield and composite. Label each of these volcanoes. Then, on the lines below each volcano, write a description of each and how it formed. If needed, look back at the Explore section to help you.

Cinder cone volcano	Shield volcano	Composite volcano

Cinder cone volcanoes are small hills of cooled lava. Lava comes up out of the ground for a while and creates a cinder cone.

Shield volcanoes form when lava flows out of a low volcanic hill over time. The lava may spread across land for quite a distance. Shield volcanoes have gentle slopes.

Composite volcanoes form from both lava flows and cinder rocks.

Label the magma chamber, vent and crater on the picture of the volcano below.

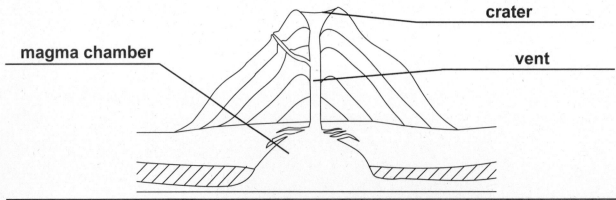

crater

magma chamber

vent

Learning Coach Guide
Lesson 8: Earthquakes

Earthquakes are among the most destructive of nature's forces. In the past, sudden earthquakes have killed thousands--sometimes hundreds of thousands--of people. To prevent such tragedies, scientists have worked hard to understand why, and where, earthquakes happen. Your student will learn about the science behind earthquakes and what makes them so powerful.

Lesson Objectives

- State that an *earthquake* is the shaking or sliding of the Earth's surface.
- Explain how a *seismograph* is used to determine earthquake activity.
- Describe how the *Richter scale* is used to measure an earthquake's magnitude.

PREPARE

Approximate lesson time is 60 minutes.

Materials

For the Student

▣ Model Seismograph

cardboard box - 30 cm (12 in) each side

hole punch - (single punch)

household item - Paper cup, 5 oz. (2)

marbles

marker, black water soluble

paper, adding machine tape

pencil

ruler, metric

scissors

string

tape, masking

▣ Earthquake!

household item - glue

household item - paper

thumbtacks

wood block - 2 of same size

Lesson Notes

An earthquake is one of nature's most dramatic events. Earthquakes start as shock waves deep inside the Earth, more than 100 kilometers underground. When they rise to the surface they make the rocks and soil move up and down or back and forth, often violently. Sometimes the ground actually rolls in waves that displace everything in their path.

The Mechanics of an Earthquake

The point underground where an earthquake begins is called the *focus*. The focus is nearly always on a *fault*-- the boundary between continental and/or oceanic plates. Underground movement creates stress in the rock layers, and this stress may build up over hundreds or thousands of years. Then, at some point, the rock layers break abruptly and a tremendous amount of energy is released.

This energy moves away from the focus in waves, and if the waves are powerful enough they reach the surface. The place on the surface directly above the focus is called the *epicenter*. The waves have their most powerful effect at the epicenter, but they keep spreading out from the epicenter and move far away.

Tools for Studying Earthquakes

Scientists study earthquakes to help them predict where an earthquake might occur next and how destructive it might be. One of the measures scientists use to assess the power of a quake is the *Richter scale*. The largest quake ever recorded in modern times measured 8.6 on the Richter scale. Seismologists use a *seismograph* to measure earthquake waves. The machine records the magnitude of a quake, and is used in conjunction with other machines to locate the epicenter. By reading three or more seismographs set up in different locations, seismologists can easily find the epicenter.

When an earthquake strikes the bottom of the ocean, an unusual thing can happen. The earthquake can set up an extremely powerful ocean wave. Though some call this a *tidal wave*, it has nothing to do with tides. It is also called a *seismic sea wave*, but many people know it by its Japanese name--*tsunami*, which means *harbor wave*. In the open ocean you would hardly notice a tsunami. Your boat would rise about a meter, and a while later it would drop a meter. The distance between tsunami wave crests can be as much as 700 km (435 miles). But when this long, low wave enters shallow water, it piles up. A tsunami near the shore can rise more than 30 meters (100 feet). Tsunamis are incredibly destructive. In the Alaskan earthquake of 1964, nine people died as a result of the earthquake tremors, but 107 lives were taken by the resulting tsunamis.

Keywords and Pronunciation

epicenter : The point on the Earth's surface that is right above the focus of an earthquake. The greatest damage was done at the epicenter of the quake.

fault : A break in the Earth's crust along which plates move. The San Andreas Fault in California is the site of many earthquakes.

focus : The point where the movement of the plates started. The earthquake that caused so much damage had a focus deep within the Earth.

Richter (RIHK-tuhr)

seismograph (SIYZ-muh-graf) : An instrument used to record earthquake waves. The seismograph recorded a large earthquake at 10:05 a.m.

seismologist (siyz-MAH-luh-jist)

tsunami (tsou-NAH-mee)

TEACH
Activity 1: The Big Shake (Online)
Instructions

Have your student read through the Explore on her own. Reinforce and explain difficult concepts as needed.

Explore Suggestions:

Screen 3: As review from the last lesson, ask your student to explain what can happen when plates move against each other.

Screen 6: Ask your student if she remembers what the Ring of Fire is known for besides earthquakes (volcanoes).

After this activity, check to see if your student can do the following:

- State that an *earthquake* is the shaking or sliding of the Earth's surface.
- Explain how a *seismograph* is used to determine earthquake activity.
- Describe how the *Richter scale* is used to measure an earthquake's magnitude.

If your student has difficulty with any of these concepts, you may wish to review the Explore with her and have her explain the key points on each screen.

Safety

As usual, you may wish to preview any books or websites listed in this lesson.

Activity 2: Model Seismograph (Offline)
Instructions

Teaching:

Scientists use a sensitive instrument called a *seismograph* to record earthquake activity. When an earthquake shakes the ground it generates seismic waves, which can be recorded on a seismograph. The record of ground shaking recorded by the seismograph is called a *seismogram.*

A needle filled with ink draws lines on paper that runs through the machine. When the activity increases, the lines on the paper go up and down drastically. The stronger the earthquake, the more variation is seen in the lines.

Your student will need your help to build her own seismograph. She will be able to simulate an earthquake as she shakes the box.

Troubleshooting:

You student may not be able to cut the hole and the slits in the box by herself. Have her trace their dimensions first, and then help her cut them out. When it is time to simulate the earthquake, you may want to help by shaking the box as your student pulls the paper. Do not shake the box too hard, however, or the marker will go off the edges of the paper.

What to Expect:

Your student should be able to observe the zigzag pattern drawn on the paper as you shook the box. The lines on the paper "peak" and "valley," showing that there is earthquake activity. During the second earthquake, the zigzag of the lines should be even more drastic, showing that the second earthquake has a higher magnitude than the first. Your student should be able to explain that seismologists use the Richter scale to measure the magnitude of an earthquake.

ASSESS

Lesson Assessment: Earthquakes (*Online*)

Students will complete an online assessment based on the lesson objectives. The assessment will be scored by the computer. The attached answer key is the most current and may not coincide with previously printed guides.

TEACH

Activity 3. Optional: Earthquake! (*Offline*)

Instructions

Your student will make a model of an earthquake using two wooden blocks, a piece of paper, and some thumbtacks. She will glue the paper to the blocks and place the thumbtacks upside down on top.

Answers:

1. The blocks represent two continental plates sliding past each other.
2. When you push the blocks in opposite directions, the paper will resist, then suddenly tear, flipping the tacks.
3. Your student should be able to explain that this is similar to what happens during a real earthquake because the shaking of the ground--caused by the blocks moving in opposite directions--cracked the surface of the Earth (the paper) and made the tacks move.

Safety

Caution your student to be careful when working with the thumbtacks in the Beyond the Lesson activity.

Learning Coach Guide
Lesson 9: Unit Review and Assessment

The United States Geological Survey (USGS), is a government agency that collects, monitors, and analyzes information about natural resources in the United States and around the world. They have an information center people can call to ask questions about rocks, minerals, volcanoes, earthquakes--anything about the Earth.

Your student will be asked to act as a volunteer at the call center. As she takes "calls," she will be reviewing the information taught in this unit to prepare her for the Unit Assessment.

Lesson Objectives

- Explain that rock is composed of different combinations of minerals.
- Recognize that you can identify minerals by their color, luster, hardness, streak, and specific gravity.
- Identify and describe the properties of the Earth's layers: crust, mantle, outer core, and inner core.
- Recognize that minerals have their own distinct crystal shape, determined by the arrangement of their atoms.
- Differentiate among igneous, sedimentary, and metamorphic rocks by referring to their properties and methods of formation.
- Explain that the surface of the Earth is made up of rigid plates that are in constant motion, and that the motion of these plates against, over, and under each other causes earthquakes, volcanoes, and the formation of mountains.
- Identify the various structures of volcanoes, describe the types of eruptions that form them, and explain how they change the landscape.
- Describe what happens during an earthquake and how the landscape can change as a result.
- Recognize that ore is rock with a high metal content, and that most metals come from minerals mined from the Earth's crust.
- Explain how a *seismograph* is used to determine earthquake activity.
- Describe how the *Richter scale* is used to measure an earthquake's magnitude.

PREPARE

Approximate lesson time is 60 minutes.

TEACH
Activity 1: On Call! *(Online)*

Instructions

Have your student read through the Explore on her own. Reinforce and explain difficult concepts as needed.

Explore Suggestions:

Your student will review some of the key concepts presented in this unit, along with some of the illustrations and photos used in the lessons. Have her read through the Explore on her own. Reinforce and explain difficult concepts as needed.

After this activity, check to see if your student can do the following:

- Identify and describe the properties of the Earth's layers: crust, mantle, outer core, and inner core.
- Explain that rock is composed of different combinations of minerals.
- Recognize that minerals have their own distinct crystal shape, determined by the arrangement of their atoms.
- Recognize that you can identify minerals by their color, luster, hardness, streak, and specific gravity.
- Recognize that *ore* is rock with a high metal content, and that most metals come from minerals mined from the Earth's crust.
- Differentiate among igneous, sedimentary, and metamorphic rocks by referring to their properties and methods of formation.
- Explain that the surface of the Earth is made up of rigid plates that are in constant motion, and that the motion of these plates against, over, and under each other causes earthquakes, volcanoes, and the formation of mountains.
- Identify the various structures of volcanoes, describe the types of eruptions that form them, and explain how they change the landscape.
- Describe what happens during an earthquake and how the landscape can change as a result.

If your student has difficulty with any of these concepts, you may wish to review the Explore sections of the lessons in this unit with her and have her explain the key points on each screen.

ASSESS

Unit Assessment: Rocks and Minerals (*Offline*)

Students will complete an offline Unit Assessment. Print the assessment and have students complete it on their own. Use the answer key to score the assessment, and then enter the results online. The attached answer key is the most current and may not coincide with previously printed guides.

Name _____ Date _____

Rocks and Minerals Unit Assessment Answer Key

1. In the space below, draw a picture of the Earth and label the four
   main layers. Then describe the properties of each layer on the lines
   below. **(8 points; 1 point each)**

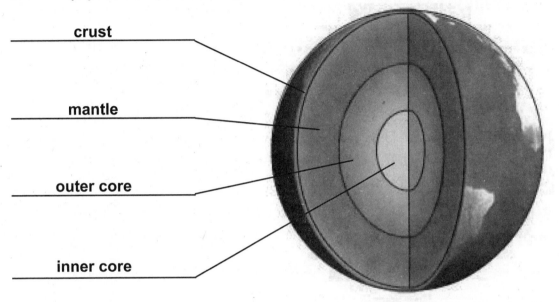

crust

mantle

outer core

inner core

crust **Answers may vary but should include: The crust is the thin, hard,**
    rocky, outer layer of the Earth.

mantle **Answers may vary but should include: The mantle is between the**
    outer core and the crust. It is made of solid rock, but is under so much
    pressure that it is constantly moving.

outer core **Answers may vary but should include: The outer core is**
    made mostly of liquid iron.

inner core **The inner core is an extremely hot layer that scientists think is**
    made of mostly solid iron.

Rocks and Minerals Unit Assessment Answer Key

2. How are rocks different from minerals? __(2 points) Answers may vary but__
__should include: Minerals are solids that form in the Earth's crust and have__
__a regular chemical composition. Rock is made up of two or more minerals.__
__Rocks may be made of minerals, glass, and organic matter.__

3. The Earth is made up of rigid plates that are always moving. As these
plates move, they can cause earthquakes to occur and mountains
and volcanoes to form. In the spaces below, describe how the
moving plates cause each to happen.   **(6 points; 2 points each)**

mountains __Answers may vary but should include: When two continental__
__plates collide, they push and push, until the land at the boundary gets__
__folded and rises up. As the plates continue to collide, a mountain will form__
__and continue to grow bigger and bigger.__

volcanoes __When an oceanic plate collides with a continent plate, the__
__oceanic plate forces its way under the continental plate. The rocks that__
__make up the oceanic plate are forced down so far that they melt. The crust__
__is so unstable at this kind of boundary that magma may break through the__
__crust, causing a volcano to erupt.__

earthquakes __When two plates slide against each other in opposite__
__directions, an earthquake may occur.__

Rocks and Minerals Unit Assessment Answer Key

4. Earthquakes occur in different places around the world, especially in the areas within the Ring of Fire. Explain what happens to the Earth's surface during an earthquake, and how an earthquake can change the landscape around it.   **(2 points) Answers may vary but should**

 include: As the two continental plates slide against each other, stress is

 created in the rock layers. This stress causes the rock layers to break,

 and a tremendous amount of energy is released. The waves of energy

 hit the surface of the Earth and can cause landslides, cracks in the

 ground, or damage to buildings and roads.

5. Write *true* in front of each true statement. Write *false* in front of each false statement. **(3 points; 1 point each)**

    _____**false**_____ All minerals have the same type of crystal structure because all of their atoms are arranged the same way.

    _____**true**_____ Ore is a mineral that contains a large amount of metal. Most minerals come from rock that is mined from the Earth's crust.

    _____**true**_____ Scientists identify minerals by their color, luster, hardness, streak, and specific gravity.

6. Write the word from the Word Bank next to the statement that matches it. **(12 points; 1 point each)**

    Word Bank

cinder cone	Richter scale	vent	sedimentary
composite	volcano	ore	metamorphic
magma chamber	crater	igneous	shield
seismograph	earthquake		

Rocks and Minerals Unit Assessment Answer Key

magma chamber The central collecting place for magma at the base of the volcano.

composite This towering volcano forms from both lava flows and cinder rocks.

seismograph A tool scientists use to measure earthquake activity.

ore Rock with a high metal content.

sedimentary These rocks form when bits of rock are compacted by pressure and cement together to form new rocks.

crater This is the top of the volcano where sulfur-filled gasses and lava come out.

shield This type of volcano forms as lava spreads over a long distance and cools to form a hill with gentle slopes.

metamorphic These rocks form when other rocks are subjected to large amounts of pressure, heat, or chemical reactions.

Richter scale Scientists use this to measure the magnitude of an earthquake.

igneous These rocks form in volcanoes and wherever magma pushes through the crust.

cinder cone When lava comes up out of the ground for a long period of time, this type of volcano is formed.

vent This stony tube runs up the center of the volcano. It may have many branches though which lava flows during an eruption.

Learning Coach Guide
Lesson 1: Weathering

Rocks and minerals are formed and broken down in the turbulent processes of Earth. Rocks formed in huge eruptions of lava may slowly fade away under forces of weathering--wind, water, and even the workings of living things. These bits of rocks and minerals may form huge sediments. So the Earth, which seems so unchanging is, in fact, always changing.

Your student will begin to examine the processes that break down surface rocks. Physical (mechanical) and chemical weathering will be discussed as a prelude to erosion and mass wasting.

Lesson Objectives

- Identify examples of physical and chemical weathering.
- Describe different causes of weathering, such as ice, growth from plants, and acid rain.

PREPARE

Approximate lesson time is 60 minutes.

Materials

For the Student

    🖥 Physical and Chemical Weathering

    clay

    cup, plastic (3)

    freezing source

    vinegar

    chalk

    markers

    plastic wrap

    spoon (2)

    water

Lesson Notes

If one thing should be clear from your student's previous studies of the rock cycle, continental drift, volcanoes, and earthquakes, it is that the Earth is dynamic. Some changes happen quickly, others take centuries, but the surface of our planet is always in flux.

In these next few lessons your student will examine three major ways in which the surface of the Earth changes:

- *Weathering*--The process by which rocks are broken down. Various factors cause rocks to disintegrate into pebbles, soil, and dust.
- *Erosion*--The movement of soil and broken rocks by wind, water, or even glaciers.
- *Mass wasting* --The movement of rocks or soil down a slope by the force of gravity. This includes mudslides and rockslides.

Here the focus is on weathering:

- *Weathering* is the process by which rocks are broken down to pebbles or soil, by either physical or chemical means.
- The *physical weathering,* also called *mechanical weathering,* of rocks is their breakup by mechanical means.

One obvious example of mechanical weathering is the striking of one rock against another as they tumble down a hillside. More subtle factors include the repeated expansion and contraction of rocks as the sun comes up and goes down and the freezing of rainwater that has dripped into minute cracks in the rock. Some recent studies suggest this is a less common cause of mechanical weathering.

Water in motion is destructive, even without freezing. A tumbling creek seems gentle, but over time its actions can wear away the rocks in it. Rocks at the bases of waterfalls, the bends of rivers, and especially at the edge of a sea are constantly beaten by water.

Wind, especially when it carries grains of sand, is also a powerful agent in breaking apart rocks.

Finally, living things play a role in weathering. Your student may have seen a tree root that has dislodged or even cracked a huge boulder. Plant roots, even small ones, wedge themselves inside crevices in rocks and can break the rocks apart as they grow.

- *Chemical weathering* is the breakdown of a rock's minerals by chemical means.

When carbon dioxide dissolves in water, carbonic acid forms. Carbonic acid eats away at many kinds of rocks, as do other naturally occurring acids.

Lichens are a combination of fungi and algae that grows on the surface of rocks. They secrete acids that eat away at rock.

Acids from factories are released into atmosphere and become part of raindrops. As rain hits the rocks it deposits the destructive acids.

The rate at which rock is broken down depends on many factors. Rocks in tropical areas are affected by great extremes of moisture. In addition, plants break down rocks in the tropics at an accelerated rate.

Keywords and Pronunciation

deposition : The dumping of soil or rock particles in a place far from their origins. The glacier caused the deposition of a huge amount of weathered rock at the mouth of the river.

erosion : The movement of soil and broken rocks by wind, water, or other means. During the Dust Bowl era, wind caused great erosion of the soil.

lichen (*LIY-kuhn*)

mass wasting : The movement down a slope of a body of rock and/or soil due directly to gravity. Mass wasting can be rapid, as when a landslide or mudflow occurs, or it can be slower, as in a slow creep of a hillside downhill.

sediment : The layers of rock or soil that result from their transport and deposition. The sediment at the bottom of the lake originated as soil on the nearby hills.

weathering : the breakdown of rocks by physical or chemical processes; weathering causes the rocks on a cliff to wear away

TEACH
Activity 1: The Breakdown of Rocks *(Online)*
Instructions
Have your student read through the Explore on his own. Reinforce and explain difficult concepts as needed.

Explore Suggestions:

Screen 4:You can use a fan or hair dryer to simulate wind erosion. Make a stack of cotton balls and turn the fan or hair dryer on low. Your student can use a meter stick to measure how far the "wind" carries the cotton balls.

Screen 5: Go on a nature walk and see if you can find any lichens growing on a rock. Ask your student to explain how the lichen is changing the rock.

After this activity, check to see if your student can do the following:
- Identify examples of physical and chemical weathering.
- Describe different causes of weathering, such as ice, growth from plants, and acid rain.

If your student has difficulty with any of these concepts, you may wish to review the Explore with him and have him explain the key points on each screen.

Activity 2: Physical and Chemical Weathering *(Offline)*
Instructions
Teaching:

Your student will perform two activities simulating physical and chemical weathering. Both activities will take some time before the weathering is apparent. Remind your student to check on the experiments and answer the questions that follow.

Troubleshooting:

If the clay ball in the freezer does not have visible cracking, wet it again and place it back in the freezer. Weathering effects will be more dramatic with thin, dustless chalk. Sidewalk chalk will not weather as quickly or as much.

What to Expect:

Activity 1:

After 24 hours, the ball of clay that you placed in the freezer should look cracked and broken up. The water that you put on the clay froze and made the clay crack. This is an example of a type of physical weathering called *frost wedging*.

Activity 2:

When you first pour the vinegar over the chalk, your student should be able to see bubbles form. The vinegar will eventually dissolve the chalk because vinegar is a mild acid. The chalk in the water may have dissolved because water often contains weak acids. These are examples of chemical weathering similar to that caused by acid rain.

ASSESS

Lesson Assessment: Weathering (*Online*)
Students will complete an online assessment based on the lesson objectives. The assessment will be scored by the computer. The attached answer key is the most current and may not coincide with previously printed guides.

Learning Coach Guide
Lesson 2: Soils

Soils allow for plant growth and thus are the basis for agriculture. They are also much more than this. They are home to untold life forms, from earthworms to bacteria to ground beetles. It may surprise your student to learn that soils are very distinct. If you dig down into soil you will find a least five different layers, each distinct in its own way.

Lesson Objectives

- Describe a soil profile and explain how different horizons are formed.
- Describe properties of various soil types.

PREPARE

Approximate lesson time is 60 minutes.

Advance Preparation

- For this science lesson, you will need three 2-liter plastic bottles.

Materials

For the Student

🖳 What's in Your Soil?

bottle, plastic - (2 liter) (3)

household item - craft stick

household item - newspaper

household item - shovel

soil - samples

magnifying glass

markers - permanent

plastic wrap

ruler, metric

scissors

Lesson Notes

Soil is a mixture. It contains:

- Minerals, which are the "parent material" of soil and which come from the breakup of rocks
- Organic matter, which is the remains of once-living things, including plants, animals, fungi, and bacteria
- Water
- Air

Different types of soil vary in the amounts of these four components.

Rocks are broken up by both physical and chemical means. As rocks become pulverized, wind and water carry the pieces away. These bits of rocks and minerals come together to form soil.

- Pulverized rocks and minerals are called soil's *parent material*.

Parent material of soils can be of three types:

- Clay
- Sand
- Silt

These are known as soil *textures*. Sandy soils have relatively large mineral particles; clay has small particles; silts have medium-sized particles. When all three of these are mixed, the soil is known as *loam*. The organic matter that is mixed into soil is known as *humus*. Humus is formed from both the dead and decaying bodies of living things. Humus contains nutrients critical to plants. A soil rich in humus is one in which plants will grow quickly. Your student may be surprised by this idea at first, but air and water are essential parts of soil. They fill the spaces between soil particles. Soils rich in sand and silt have large spaces, and thus a good deal of air and water. This makes them good for plants. Clay soils, by contrast, have very small particles, less air and water, and may slow down the growth of plants.

Different ecosystems often have their own types of soil, with their own unique blends of parent material, humus, air, and water. Scientists have named many different soil types.

Soils also differ not only in type but also in how they are arranged from the surface down. If you dig straight down and then look at the soil from the side you may see as many as five or six layers.

- Taken together, all these layers make up what geologists call the *soil profile*.
- Each layer is given a letter, representing what is called a *soil horizon*.

These horizons are displayed graphically in the lesson. They are:

O horizon --This is the uppermost layer, including decaying material.

A horizon--Earthworms, ants, ground beetles, plant roots, and many other factors cause parent material and humus to mix here. The O and A horizons make up the *topsoil*.

E horizon --This layer contain much less humus than the A horizon. Draining water carries small rock fragments to this layer.

B horizon--This layer is the result of small particles moving through the soil, a process called *leeching*. Water may have a hard time moving though this horizon, or, once there, may remain in the clay for a long time.

C horizon--This layer is made up of partially broken rock. The B and C layers together are called the *subsoil*.

Keywords and Pronunciation

fertile : Capable of supporting plant growth. The gardener said that the lush growth of petunias was due to the fertile soil.

horizon : One of the layers in a soil profile. The A horizon of my soil sample was loaded with earthworms and ants.

humus (HYOO-muhs) : Organic matter in the soil, which is the remains of decayed and decaying living things. The farmer was happy with the new land because the soil was rich in humus.

TEACH
Activity 1: Amazing Soil *(Online)*

Instructions
Have your student read through the Explore on his own. Reinforce and explain difficult concepts as needed.

Explore Suggestions:
Screen 4: Reinforce with your student the idea that a soil profile is all of the different layers of soil combined.

Screen 5: Your student will not need to name each horizon by letter, but he should be able to explain that soil is made up of different layers and what is found in some of the layers.

Screen 6: Your student should be able to describe the things found in the topsoil. Topsoil is made up of the two top layers in a soil profile, which contain decaying material from living things. It is in this layer that plants get most of the nutrients they need to live and grow.

After this activity, check to see if your student can:
- Describe a soil profile and explain how different horizons are formed.
- Describe properties of various soil types.

If your student has difficulty with any of these concepts, you may wish to review the Explore with him and have him explain the key points on each screen.

Activity 2: What's in Your Soil? *(Offline)*
Instructions
Teaching:

Have your student go outside and collect several soil samples to study. He should collect them from different areas, such as from a garden, in the woods, or from the front yard. He will study the different soils with a magnifying glass and do a water study that makes the organic material float to the top.

Troubleshooting:

Help your student to dig at least 6-8 inches down to reach the next horizon for each soil sample. If the horizon layers are present, your student will be able to see them before the soil is spread on the newspaper. If needed, have him refer back to the Explore section and review what is found in the different horizon layers. If your student is unable to identify what type of parent material is contained in the samples, have him rub some of the soil between his fingers. Sandy soils feel gritty. Silt-like soils do not feel rough at all. Clay soils feel hard and smooth when dry, but sticky when wet.

What to Expect:

Your student should find all sorts of rocks and organic material in the soil samples. When the samples are allowed to sit for a day under water, the organic material should float to the top. The sample taken from a garden, or an area that has a lot of plants around it, should contain more organic material than the other samples. Your student should also be able to recognize what type of parent material is contained in the samples.

Safety

Be careful where you help your student dig up the soil. Check with your local utility company to find out where electrical lines may be buried.

ASSESS

Lesson Assessment: Soils (*Offline*)

Students will complete an offline assessment based on the lesson objectives. Print the assessment and have students complete it on their own. Use the answer key to score the assessment, and then enter the results online. The attached answer key is the most current and may not coincide with previously printed guides.

Name _____ Date _____

Soil Assessment Answer Key

Jim and Laura need your help. They have always dreamed of owning their own farm where they can grow their own crops. They want to start looking for a piece of property to start their farm on, but they heard that they need to make sure the soil is good for planting. Jim and Laura know that there are different types of soil, but they don't know much about each of them. Answer Jim and Laura's questions below to help them out. Use the illustration to help you.

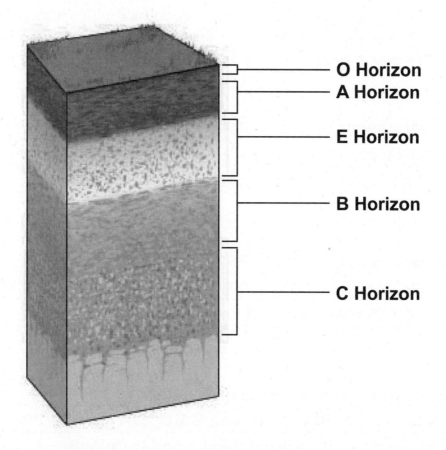

O Horizon
A Horizon
E Horizon
B Horizon
C Horizon

Jim wants to know what a soil profile is. Can you explain it to him? _____
Answers may vary but should include: A soil profile is all the different
layers that can be seen if you dig straight down and then look at the
soil sample from the side. There may be as many as five or six layers.
Each layer is made up of different materials and has its own unique
properties.

☼ Assessment

Soil Assessment Answer Key

Laura knows that the top two layers of a soil profile are called *topsoil*. What are some of the things that can be found in the topsoil? _____
_____**Answers may vary but should include: Topsoil contains**_____
_____**decaying material, earthworms, ants, ground beetles, plant**_____
_____**roots and a mixture of parent material and humus.**_____

_____

Both Jim and Laura don't know much about the different types of soil. Jim thinks that clay soil is the best kind to grow crops in, but Laura thinks that sand and silt are the best types of soil for plants. Explain the different types of soil for them. Be sure to let them know which type(s) of soil are best them to plant their crops in.

Clay:___**Answers may vary but should include: Clay soils have very**___
_____**small mineral particles. There is less air and water in clay than**_____
_____**in the other soils. Clay is good for pottery and ceramics.**_____

_____

Silt:___**Answers may vary but should include: Silt soils have medium-**___
_____**sized mineral particles. They have large spaces that hold a lot of**_____
_____**air and water. This makes silt good for plants.**_____

_____

Sand:___**Answers may vary but should include: Sandy soils have large**___
_____**mineral particles. A great deal of air and water can get into the**_____
_____**large spaces in sandy soils making them good for plants.**_____

_____

Learning Coach Guide
Lesson 3: Erosion and Deposition: Gravity and Water

Rocks seem solid to us, but now we know that rock can be destroyed by weathering and become the parent material for soil. Soil too is part of the great recycling of rocks and minerals, for soil can be swept away and transported by the forces of gravity and water. See some of the forces that are behind erosion and mass wasting.

Lesson Objectives

- Describe how the slope of the land affects erosion.
- Describe how gravity and moving water weather, erode, and shape the surface of the land by transporting sediment from one location to another, where it is deposited.

PREPARE

Approximate lesson time is 60 minutes.

Materials

For the Student

🖳 Water Erosion

clay - modeling

cup, plastic - 8 oz

drinking glass

drinking straw

household item - 3 books

soil

cookie sheet

measuring cup

paper towels

pencil

water

Lesson Notes

Chemical and physical weathering breaks down rocks. When this happens, pulverized rocks and their minerals become part of the soil. Soil is not static, though. It changes and moves over time.

Soil is moved by two processes, erosion and mass wasting. When that mass of rock and soil is eventually deposited in another spot, the overall process is called *deposition*.

Four major forces are involved in erosion and mass wasting

- *Gravity*--The same force that pulls any mass toward the center of the Earth pulls down material.
- *Water*--Material is carried away from its starting place by the force of rain or by powerful streams.
- *Glaciers*--Materials are pushed or carried, often long distances, by glacial movement.
- *Wind*--Small particles are carried vast distances by the mechanical action of wind.

Here your student will examine the first two of these: gravity and water.

Gravity's effects on soil can be fast or slow, depending on the soil. For example, loose or pebbly soil may erode under gravity's pull faster than hard clay soil.

The roots of plants help hold the soil in place, preventing erosion.

- When gravity's effects are sudden and large amounts of earth move, we call it *mass wasting*.

When a raindrop lands, it loosens the soil. As rain continues to fall, the water collects in little trickles called *rills*.

- Rills flow into each other and form small gullies.
- Gullies join one another to form a creek.
- Creeks flow together forming rivers. Rivers that flow into larger rivers are called *tributaries*.

At each of these stages some soil is washed away. If the land surrounding a river erodes easily, the river will carry all the eroded soil in its waters. This is called *sediment*.

Every stream and every river carries sediment, some more than others. This is one of the main characteristics of erosion by water--the soil is carried far from its origin.

Eventually, though, deposition happens. At some point, in a lake or an ocean, the sediment settles to the bottom and forms a new layer of earth.

Keywords and Pronunciation

deposition : The settling of rock and soil after it has been transported by forces causing erosion. The river was blocked by the deposition of soil after the mudslide.

erosion : The movement of soil and rock by agents such as gravity, water, glaciers, and wind. The Badlands of South Dakota show evidence of erosion by wind.

mass wasting : The movement down a slope of a body of rock and/or soil due directly to gravity. Mass wasting can be rapid, as when a landslide or mudflow occurs, or it can be slower, as in a slow creep of a hillside downhill.

tributary : A smaller river or creek that carries water into a larger river. The Ohio River is a tributary of the Mississippi River.

V-shaped valley : A valley shaped like a V in cross section, the shape of which is caused by water. Many valleys in California are V-shaped valleys, formed by rushing water.

TEACH
Activity 1: Powers of Gravity and Water *(Online)*
Instructions

Have your student read through the Explore on his own. Reinforce and explain difficult concepts as needed.

Explore Suggestions:

Screen 3: Be sure that your student can differentiate between a earthslide, a mudslide, and a rockslide.

Screen 4: Ask your student to explain how sediment that starts in a trickle or rill of rainwater makes its way to a big river.

Screen 5: Review what soil horizons are with your student. He should be able to tell you some of the materials that can be found in the different layers.

After this activity, check to see if your student can:

- Describe how the slope of the land affects erosion.
- Describe how gravity and moving water weather, erode, and shape the surface of the land by transporting sediment from one location to another and depositing it there.

If your student has difficulty with any of these concepts, you may wish to review the Explore with him and have him explain the key points on each screen.

Activity 2: Water Erosion *(Offline)*
Instructions
Teaching:

This is an outdoor activity. Your student will experiment with different slopes to see how they affect erosion. A cookie sheet covered in dirt will represent the land. Your student will change the slope of the land by placing a book under one end of the cookie sheet. A water-filled paper cup with a straw spigot will act as the source of rainfall. Adding a second and then third book under the cookie sheet will increase the slope in each trial.

Troubleshooting:

Be sure your student uses the same amount of soil and places the cup at the same spot for each trial. The cookie sheet should be dried off between each trial.

What to Expect:

Your student should observe the soil or sediment being washed down the slope by water and gravity. The sediment is transported by the water and deposited at the bottom of the slope. Your student should be able to explain that more sediment is washed away as the slope is increased.

Extension:

Have your student repeat the experiment using different soils, such as humus, clay, sand, or silt to see if the type of soil affects the amount of erosion that water and gravity can cause.

ASSESS

Lesson Assessment: Erosion and Deposition: Gravity and Water (*Online*)

Students will complete an online assessment based on the lesson objectives. The assessment will be scored by the computer. The attached answer key is the most current and may not coincide with previously printed guides.

Learning Coach Guide
Lesson 4: Erosion, Transport, and Deposition: Glaciers and Wind

We continue with our examination of the forces of erosion by discussing glacial and wind erosion. Glaciers are somewhat far from our common experience, but many people in North American live on lands that were shaped by glaciers in the past. The erosion and deposition of rocks and soils by glaciers has shaped the land we live on. Wind is a more daily factor causing erosion, and can be particularly influential in dry areas.

Lesson Objectives

- Describe how glaciers are formed and differentiate between the continental and valley glaciers.
- Explain how glaciers move to erode and reshape the surface of the land.
- Describe how wind erodes and weathers the surface of the land.

PREPARE

Approximate lesson time is 60 minutes.

Advance Preparation

- You will need to prepare an ice block ahead of time for this science lesson. Place a cup of water with bits of sand, gravel, and clay into a plastic container and place in the freezer overnight.

Materials

For the Student

⌨ Glaciers

cardboard box - top, large with sides

clay

freezing source

gravel

household item - additional lamp

household item - plastic container

household item - plastic container top

sand

soil

lamp

ruler

water

Lesson Notes

A glacier is a mass of ice that has built up over many years. Different kinds of glaciers exist:

- *Valley glacier*--Formed between mountains so that it is shaped like a wedge, or a giant U. When the ice melts, a U-shaped valley remains.
- *Alpine glacier*--Formed on the tops and sides of significantly tall mountains.
- *Continental ice sheet*--Formed during ice ages. These can cover thousands of square miles of land. Antarctica and Greenland currently have such ice sheets.

Glaciers can move, and cause huge amounts of erosion when they do so.

One kind of motion happens in the glaciers that form in mountainous areas. When the glacier's mass becomes great enough, it slides slowly down the mountain. Glaciers may only move a few yards a year, but the effect over time is significant.

A second kind of motion occurs after glacial ice is about 200 feet thick. At this point the glacier begins to compact itself. The ice pushes out the front and sides.

During the last ice age a continental ice sheet covered much of North America. As the glaciers retreated, they left behind a landscape completely changed by erosion.

As a glacier moves across the land, it pushes soil and rocks in front of it and to the sides of it, much like an enormous plow. When it melts again this pushed-aside soil is left in long hills. Pushing an object through a sandbox and then lifting the object up will show this effect.

- The hills formed by glaciers are called *moraines*.
- Soil pushed in front of a glacier is called an *end moraine*.
- Soil pushed to the sides forms *lateral moraines*.
- Glaciers also gouge the Earth as they move, leaving behind *kettle lakes*.

Wind may seem a less-dramatic force to your student than glaciers, but it works relentlessly and is a very significant factor in erosion.

In dry areas the particles of soil do not stick together. Wind can blow these light particles hundreds of miles. This kind of erosion is prevented by a good covering of plants, known as *ground cover*.

The process of wind sweeping over the soil is called *deflation*.

As it sweeps the land, wind picks up small bits of rock, mineral, or soils, leaving only things too heavy to be lifted. This can result in dry, pebbly ground. Such land is called *desert pavement*.

All this rock and soil is deposited when the wind drops it again. In some areas, such as the central US and Canada, huge hills and sand dunes have been formed entirely out of soil dropped there by wind.

Keywords and Pronunciation

glacier (GLAY-shur) : A mass of ice that arises from years of snow adding up. The glacier ended at the ocean where huge chunks of ice fell into the sea.

moraine (muh-RAYN) : The mass of earth and ice pushed to the front or side of a moving glacier. Most of the high ports in northern Long Island in New York State are parts of an old moraine.

U-shaped valley : A valley that is rounded at the bottom; formed and given its characteristic shape by a glacier that once inhabited it. There are many U-shaped valleys in Alaska.

TEACH
Activity 1: The Power of Ice and Wind (Online)
Instructions
Have your student read through the Explore on his own. Reinforce and explain difficult concepts as needed.

Explore Suggestions:

Screen 4: Ask your student to explain how plants can help prevent wind erosion.

Screen 5: If you haven't already done so, use a hairdryer or fan to experiment with wind erosion. Have your student test different types of soil, including soil that contains plants, to see which is affected by wind erosion the most.

After this activity, check to see if your student can do the following:

- Describe how glaciers are formed and differentiate between the continental and valley glaciers.
- Explain how glaciers, by moving, erode and reshape the surface of the land.
- Describe how wind erodes and weathers the surface of the land.

If your student has difficulty with any of these concepts, you may wish to review the Explore with him and have him explain the key points on each screen.

Activity 2: Glacial Erosion (Offline)
Instructions
Teaching:

Glaciers erode the land, causing great changes to occur. In this activity, your student will observe how a glacier changes the landscape as it moves and erodes the Earth's surface.

Troubleshooting:

Use as large a box top as possible. The top of a large plastic tub or container can also be used.

If you do not have a lamp that can swing over the box top, use two lamps. Place the lamps as close to the box as possible without touching it. If needed, place the box top on a small table and the lamps on the floor so the heat of the bulbs will reach the ice block.

What to Expect:

Your student starts the experiment by creating a V-shaped river valley. The valley will be U-shaped to the point where the glacier stopped, and V-shaped where it didn't travel.

The area along where the glacier moved should be smoother and have steeper sides than the part of the land where it did not travel. Your student should be able to identify the lateral and end moraines and well as any kettle lakes that may have formed.

As the glacier melted, the bits of rock, sand and clay should have been deposited along the moraines.

Based on the U-shaped valley that was created by the glacier, your student should be able to identify the glacier as a valley glacier.

ASSESS

Lesson Assessment: Erosion, Transport, and Deposition: Glaciers and Wind, Online (Online)

Students will complete an online assessment based on the lesson objectives. The assessment will be scored by the computer. The attached answer key is the most current and may not coincide with previously printed guides.

124

Learning Coach Guide
Lesson 5: Unit Review and Assessment

Your student will review for the Unit Assessment as he helps solve a mystery.

Lesson Objectives

- Describe a soil profile and explain how different horizons are formed.
- Explain both the physical and the chemical weathering of rocks, and be able to classify examples of each.
- Explain that *soil* is a mixture of weathered rock, humus, air, and water.
- Describe how gravity, moving water, wind, and glaciers weather, erode, and shape the surface of the land by transporting sediment from one location to another, where it is deposited.

PREPARE

Approximate lesson time is 60 minutes.

TEACH
Activity 1: Weathering Mystery *(Online)*
Instructions

Have your student read through the Explore on his own. Reinforce and explain difficult concepts as needed.

Explore Suggestions:

Screen 2 and 3: If your student is having difficulty answering these questions, you may want to review the Explore section of the Erosion and Deposition: Gravity and Water lesson.

Screen 5 and 6: If your student is having difficulty answering these questions, you may want to review the Explore section of the Soils lesson.

After this activity, check to see if your student can do the following:

1. Classify physical and chemical weathering of rocks. Explain both the physical and the chemical weathering of rocks.
2. Describe a soil profile and explain how different horizons are formed.
3. Explain that *soil* is a mixture of weathered rock, humus, air, and water.
4. Describe how gravity, moving water, wind, and glaciers weather, erode, and shape the surface of the land by transporting sediment from one location and depositing it in another.

If your student has difficulty with any of these concepts, you may wish to review the Explore with him and have him explain the key points on each screen.

ASSESS

Unit Assessment: Weather, Erosion, Deposition *(Offline)*

Students will complete an offline Unit Assessment. Print the assessment and have students complete it on their own. Use the answer key to score the assessment, and then enter the results online. The attached answer key is the most current and may not coincide with previously printed guides.

Name _____   Date _____

Weathering, Erosion, and Deposition Unit Assessment

Weathering, erosion, and deposition cause changes to the Earth's surface. Gravity, running water, glaciers, and wind all play a part in shaping the land. On the lines below, explain what each of them is and describe some of the changes they cause.

1. glaciers: **Answers may vary but should include: Glaciers are great masses of ice that form over thousands of years. As the glaciers move, or begin to melt, they push the sediment in front of them and off to the sides. The sediment then forms hills, or moraines, where the glacier deposits it.**

2. running water: **Answers may vary but should include: As running water, such as that in a river, passes along, it carries pieces of sediment with it and deposits them again along the way. Water that is constantly beating against rocks will ultimately cause them to break apart.**

3. gravity: **Answers may vary but should include: The force of gravity pulls sediment from areas of higher elevation to those of lower elevation. This can occur as a landslide, mudslide, slump, or rockslide.**

4. wind: **Answers may vary but should include: Wind carries small particles from the Earth's surface great distances and deposits them in a new location. Sand that is carried by the wind can also rub against rocks and wear them down.**

Weathering, Erosion, and Deposition Unit Assessment

Use the words in the Word Bank to complete the sentences below.

Word Bank

humus	sediment	profile
water	air	physical
rock	topsoil	chemical

5. Acid rain happens when carbon dioxide mixes with the water in the Earth's atmosphere. Acid rain is an example of _____ **chemical** _____ weathering.

6. Soil is a mixture of humus, weathered rock, water and _____ **air** _____.

7. If you dug a deep hole in the surface of the Earth, you would see many different layers. The layers make up the soil _____ **profile** _____.

8. Gravity, moving water, wind, and glaciers weather, erode, and shape the surface of the land by transporting _____ **sediment** _____ from one location and depositing it in another.

9. When water seeps into the cracks of a rock and then freezes, the ice pushes against the rock, causing it to split apart. This is an example of _____ **physical** _____ weathering.

10. The top two layers of a soil profile are called _____ **topsoil** _____.

Weathering, Erosion, and Deposition Unit Assessment

Label each type of erosion below as either physical or chemical and then tell what caused the erosion.

11. kind of weathering _____**chemical**_____

What caused the erosion? _____**acid**_____

12. kind of weathering _____**physical**_____

What caused the erosion? _____**gravity**_____

13. kind of weathering _____**physical**_____

What caused the erosion? _____**water**_____

14. kind of weathering _____**physical**_____

What caused the erosion? _____**glacier**_____

Learning Coach Guide
Lesson 1: Fossils and How They Form

How do we know dinosaurs and trilobites existed? And how are scientists able to figure out what the Earth looked like when these animals were alive? We can find clues in fossils left deep within layers of rock. Dig into this book and learn how fossils were formed, then meet some of the important paleontologists who use them as clues to the past.

Fossils are one piece of evidence paleontologists use to learn about the past. Through careful observation of these fossils and the information they provide, paleontologists can begin to create a picture of the Earth's history.

Lesson Objectives

- Explain that fossils provide information about organisms that lived long ago.
- State that a *fossil* is a trace, print, or remain of an organism preserved over time in a rock.
- Identify the conditions under which fossils may form.

PREPARE

Approximate lesson time is 60 minutes.

Advance Preparation

- You will need the book *The Fossil Record and the History of Life*, by Bridget Anderson, for all of the lessons in this unit. If you have not yet received this book, skip to the next unit and return to this one later.
- If you don't already have it, you will need dried black beans (1/2 cup), dried red beans (1/2 cup), and dried white beans (1/2 cup) for the Layering activity.

Materials

For the Student

Come Learn with Me: The Fossil Record and the History of Life by Bridget Anderson

📁 Layering

baking dish, rectangular - glass

food - 1/2 cup dried black beans

food - 1/2 cup dried red beans

food - 1/2 cup dried white beans

sand - 1 1/2 cups

bowl (3)

graduated cylinder

measuring cup

spoon

timer

For the Adult

📁 Layering Answer Key

Lesson Notes

If you do not have sand for the Layering activity, you may substitute potting soil.

Keywords and Pronunciation

dinosaur : Any animal belonging to a group of large reptiles that lived during the Mesozoic era. Triceratops was the largest horned dinosaur that walked the Earth.

fossil (FAH-suhl) : The trace, print, or remain of an organism preserved over time in rock. Fossils can tell us how dinosaurs looked as well as how they acted.

mammoth : A kind of ancient elephant with long, curving tusks and shaggy hair. Mammoths lived during the Ice Age.

mineral : A crystalline substance of regular atomic arrangement found in the earth. Rocks are made of two or more minerals.

paleontologist (pay-lee-ahn-TAH-luh-jist) : A scientist who studies prehistoric animal and plant life. The paleontologist examined the fossil for clues about the animal.

sedimentary rock : Rock formed from sediment (particles of sand, soil, and mud). Many fossils of dinosaurs were found deep within the sedimentary rock.

trilobite (TRIY-luh-biyt) : An extinct species of arthropod with three humps on each segment of its body. A trilobite fossil from the Paleozoic era found in the Burgess Shale gave paleontologists clues about the past.

TEACH

Activity 1: Let's Read! *(Online)*

Instructions

Have your student read pages 6-11 to learn about fossils.

Activity 2: Layering *(Offline)*

Instructions

Have your student follow the directions on the Layering sheet, which provides a hand-on experience in how fossils are formed.

ASSESS

Lesson Assessment: Fossils and How They Form (*Online*)

Students will complete an online assessment based on the lesson objectives. The assessment will be scored by the computer. The attached answer key is the most current and may not coincide with previously printed guides.

Name _____   Date _____

Layering

Follow the directions for the experiment, then answer the questions.

1. Pour 125mL (½ cup) of the white beans into a bowl.
2. Pour 125mL (½ cup) of the red beans into a second bowl.
3. Pour 125mL (½ cup) of the black beans into a third bowl.
4. Add ½ cup (125mL) of soil or sand to each bowl of beans.
5. Mix the beans and soil (or beans and sand) in each separate bowl.
6. Fill the baking dish halfway with water.
7. Slowly sprinkle the beans and soil (or beans and sand) mixture from one of the bowls into the water.
8. Wait 10 minutes and observe the layer.
9. Sprinkle the beans and soil (or beans and sand) mixture from another bowl into the water.
10. Wait 10 minutes and observe the layers now.
11. Add the last beans and soil (or beans and sand) mixture.
12. After 10 minutes, observe all three layers.

Draw the results after the final bowl of beans is added and 10 minutes have passed.

What happened to the soil or sand that was added with each bean layer? __The sand/soil all settled to the bottom of the pan.__

Consider each layer of beans a new layer of earth. Which color beans represent the oldest layer of earth? _____white_____
Why? __It is closest to the bottom.__

Which bean layer represents the youngest layer? __black__
Why? __It is closest to the top.__

Learning Coach Guide
Lesson 2: Reading the Fossil Record

Many types of fossils found within the rock layers help create the fossil record of Earth. These fossils are records of the organisms that lived together, and the rock layer is a record of clues about the environment in which the organisms lived. Learn how paleontologists use mold and cast fossils of insects, fish, and even dinosaurs, together with other evidence, to unearth clues about the Earth's past.

Lesson Objectives

- Explain that fossils help scientists reconstruct the history of life on Earth.
- State that fossils provide evidence that many kinds of organisms that once lived on Earth are now extinct.
- Identify the different types of fossils, such as petrified, cast, and mold.

PREPARE

Approximate lesson time is 60 minutes.

Advance Preparation

- If you don't already have it, you will need plaster of paris for the Make Your Own Fossil activity.

Materials

For the Student

    Come Learn with Me: The Fossil Record and the History of Life by Bridget Anderson

    🖳 Make a Fossil

    clay

    household item - paper cup

    household item - petroleum jelly

    household item - rolling pin

    household item - wax paper

    plaster of paris

    seashell

    graduated cylinder

    spoon - plastic

    timer

For the Adult

    🖳 Make a Fossil Answer Key

Keywords and Pronunciation

amber : A hard, often yellowish substance formed from fossilized tree sap. The insect was fossilized in the hardened amber.

cast fossil : A fossil formed when minerals replace animal tissue. A cast fossil is a three-dimensional view of the fossil remains.

decompose : To rot or decay. A dead animal's body will decompose over time.

decomposition : The process by which organic materials decay. Decomposition helps break down dead plants and animals.

mineralization : The process by which minerals replace the tissues of a dead organism. During mineralization, the skeleton of a dead animal hardens into rock.

paleontologist (pay-lee-ahn-TAH-luh-jist) : A scientist who studies prehistoric animal and plant life. The paleontologist examined the fossil for clues about the animal.

sedimentary : Rock formed from sediment (particles of sand, soil, and mud). Sedimentary rock is an important part of the fossilization process.

sedimentary rock : Rock formed from sediment (particles of sand, soil, and mud). Fossils are often found in sedimentary rock throughout the world.

TEACH
Activity 1: Let's Read! *(Online)*

Instructions

Have your student read pages 12-19 to learn how scientists collect and study fossil evidence.

Activity 2: Make Your Own Fossil *(Offline)*

Instructions

Have your student follow the directions on the Make a Fossil sheet to create a model of a fossil. Next, have her answer the question on the bottom of the sheet.

ASSESS
Lesson Assessment: Reading the Fossil Record (*Online*)

Students will complete an online assessment based on the lesson objectives. The assessment will be scored by the computer. The attached answer key is the most current and may not coincide with previously printed guides.

TEACH
Activity 3. Optional: Paleontologists *(Online)*

Instructions

Print the Activity Instructions if you have not already done so.

Safety

As always, you may want to preview any recommended sites before your student views them.

Name _____   Date _____

Make a Fossil

Follow the directions to make a seashell cast, then answer the question below.

1. Using a rolling pin, roll a piece of clay onto a piece of wax paper. You may choose the color. The flattened piece of clay should be about 3cm high and 5cm wide.
2. Coat the seashell with petroleum jelly and press it into the clay. Carefully remove the seashell. Wipe the excess petroleum jelly from the clay.
3. Observe the imprint the shell made. You now have a mold of the seashell.
4. Use more clay to build a wall about 1cm high around the edge of the flattened piece of clay. Secure the clay wall to the flattened piece so there are no holes under the wall. You will need the wall to hold in the plaster of Paris, which is like a thick liquid.
5. Place 70mL of the plaster of Paris into the paper cup. Slowly add about 25mL of water while mixing with the plastic spoon. The mixture should be thick but able to be poured. Add more water if necessary.
6. Fill the seashell imprint to the top of the wall with the plaster mixture.
7. Wait about 30 minutes for the plaster to dry. It should be hard when you place your finger on it.
8. Remove the clay surrounding the cast. Now you have a cast of the seashell.

What information can paleontologists learn from fossils?
Answers will vary but might include these: Scientists can learn about the size and shape of an organism that has been fossilized. The position of the fossil within the layers can tell them about the environment during the time in which the plant or animal lived.

Learning Coach Guide
Lesson 3: The Ever-Changing Earth

The Earth is constantly changing. Earthquakes shift the surface of the Earth as the oceans of the world change the shoreline of every landmass. How have the plants and animals of the Earth survived these changes? Your student will explore scientific theories about the changing world through time, and how these changes have affected living organisms.

Lesson Objectives

- State that geologic time is divided into four sections: Precambrian, Paleozoic, Mesozoic, and Cenozoic.
- Recognize that scientists think that many kinds of organisms once lived on Earth have completely disappeared.
- Recognize that scientists think that some organisms alive today resemble organisms of the distant past.

PREPARE

Approximate lesson time is 60 minutes.

Materials

For the Student

Come Learn with Me: The Fossil Record and the History of Life by Bridget Anderson

📖 Solving the Riddles of Fossils

For the Adult

📖 Solving the Riddles of Fossils Answer Key

Keywords and Pronunciation

Cenozoic (see-nuh-ZOH-ihk)

continent : A great landmass on the surface of the Earth. The United States is located on the continent of North America.

Equus : The genus name scientists give to the group of animals that include modern horses. *Equus* is the only close relative of the Hyracotherium that lives today.

evolution : The gradual change of organisms over time. Through the process of evolution, species become well adapted to life on Earth.

extinct : No longer existing. If a type of organism is extinct, it has died out.

Hyracotherium : An early ancestor of the modern horse. *Hyracotherium* was a kind of small, dog-like animal that ate mostly fruits and plants.

Mesozoic (meh-zuh-ZOH-ihk)

Paleozoic (pay-lee-uh-ZOH-ihk)

Pangaea (pan-JEE-uh) : the name scientists give to a supercontinent that once existed on earth

Precambrian (pree-KAM-bree-uhn)

species (SPEE-sheez) : A group of organisms that share many characteristics and that can interbreed. Scientists think that species slowly changed throughout history as conditions changed on Earth.

TEACH

Activity 1: Let's Read (Online)

Instructions

Have your student read pages 20-27 to learn about the very different eras of Earth's history.

Activity 2: Solving the Riddles of Fossils (Offline)

Instructions

Print Solving the Riddles of Fossils if you have not already done so. Encourage your student to use her book as necessary to answer the riddles. Remind her that paleontologists look at similar clues.

ASSESS

Lesson Assessment: The Ever-Changing Earth (Online)

Students will complete an online assessment based on the lesson objectives. The assessment will be scored by the computer. The attached answer key is the most current and may not coincide with previously printed guides.

Name _____   Date _____

Solving the Riddles of Fossils

Read each riddle, then solve it. (Hint: You'll find help in your text.)

1. I am a fossil of a fern that grew in the tropics. I was found in Antarctica, which is extremely cold. No one moved me, so why was I found in Antarctica?
   Antarctica used to be tropical. _____

2. I am a fossil of a coral that lived in the ocean. I was found on dry land, far from any ocean. If no one moved me, why would I be found in the middle of a continent?
   The sea level dropped, or land rose above the ocean's surface, so parts of the Earth that used to be ocean are now dry land.

3. I am a horse, but my ancestors didn't look anything like me. I'm much bigger than they are, and my teeth are a lot stronger. Why don't I look like earlier horses?
   Your environment changed. Your ancestors lived in a place that had lots of fruits and small plants, but you live in a grassland.

4. I am a fossil of an animal. A fossil of another animal was found in a younger layer of rock above me. He looks more like animals who are alive today than I do. Am I probably older or younger than the other fossil?
   You are probably older, mostly because you are covered by by a layer of rock that formed more recently. Living creatures change slowly, so you had to have lived a very long time ago. Not all things change, however, so not changing is not proof that the other creature is younger.

SUPER CHALLENGE: Name this era!
1. I am called the Age of Dinosaurs. **Mesozoic** _____
2. My name means *ancient life*, though sometimes I'm called the Age of Trilobites. **Paleozoic** _____
3. I am the era in which you live. **Cenozoic** _____
4. I am the longest period of geologic time.   **Precambrian** _____

Learning Coach Guide
Lesson 4: The Precambrian Time and Paleozoic Era

The Precambrian time and Paleozoic era are defined by the organisms and events of the times. While continuing the reading, your student will search into the past and uncover the worlds of the Precambrian time and Paleozoic era.

Lesson Objectives

- Name one major event that occurred during the Precambrian time.
- Name one major event that occurred during the Paleozoic era.
- Name one organism that lived on the Earth during the Precambrian time.
- Name one organism that lived on the Earth during the Paleozoic era.

PREPARE

Approximate lesson time is 60 minutes.

Materials

For the Student

Come Learn with Me: The Fossil Record and the History of Life by Bridget Anderson

What Did the Moon See?

Keywords and Pronunciation

amphibian (am-FIH-bee-uhn) : A vertebrate that spends part of its life in water and part of its life on land. Frogs, toads, and salamanders are amphibians.

brachiopod (BRAY-kee-uh-pahd)

cyanobacteria (siy-A-nuh-bak-TIHR-ee-uh) : Bacteria that were one of the first forms of life on Earth. The earliest known fossils are of cyanobacteria.

meteorite (MEE-tee-uh-riyt) : A rocky object in space that falls to Earth before it burns up. A meteorite that hit the Earth made a crater as large as a football field.

Paleozoic (pay-lee-uh-ZOH-ihk)

Pangaea (pan-JEE-uh) : the name scientists give to a supercontinent that once existed on earth

Precambrian (pree-KAM-bree-uhn)

sedimentary rock : Rock formed from sediment (particles of sand, soil, and mud). Fossils are often found in sedimentary rock throughout the world.

stromatolite : A large colony of cynabacteria that grows like a reef of coral. Colonies of cyanobacteria form stromatolites that look like stone pillars in the ocean.

stromatolites (stroh-MA-tl-iyts)

trilobite (TRIY-luh-biyt) : An extinct species of arthropod with three humps on each segment of its body. A trilobite fossil from the Paleozoic era found in the Burgess Shale gave paleontologists clues about the past.

TEACH
Activity 1: Let's Read! *(Online)*
Instructions
Have your student read pages 28-35 to discover more about the Precambrian time and Paleozoic era.

Activity 2: Diary of the Past *(Offline)*
Instructions
Print the Activity Instructions and the What Did the Moon See? sheet if you have not already done so. Encourage your student to write creative and complete answers. She should refer to the book often, and she should use all of the words in the Word Bank at the bottom of the sheet.

ASSESS

Lesson Assessment: The Precambrian Time and Paleozoic Era (*Online*)
Students will complete an online assessment based on the lesson objectives. The assessment will be scored by the computer. The attached answer key is the most current and may not coincide with previously printed guides.

Learning Coach Guide
Lesson 5: The Mesozoic and Cenozoic Eras

The Mesozoic and Cenozoic eras are defined by the organisms and events of the times. While continuing the reading, your student will search into the past and uncover the worlds of the Mesozoic and Cenozoic eras.

Lesson Objectives

- Name one major event that occurred during the Mesozoic era.
- Name one major event that occurred during the Cenozoic era.
- Name one organism that lived on the Earth during the Mesozoic era.
- Name one major event that occurred in each of the four geologic sections: Precambrian, Paleozoic, Mesozoic, and Cenozoic.

PREPARE

Approximate lesson time is 60 minutes.

Materials

For the Student

Come Learn with Me: The Fossil Record and the History of Life by Bridget Anderson

📖 When Did It Happen?

For the Adult

📖 When Did It Happen? Answer Key

Keywords and Pronunciation

asphalt : A black, tar-like substance. Asphalt fills The La Brea tar pits. Animals throughout the Cenozoic era became trapped in the tar.

Cenozoic (see-nuh-ZOH-ihk)

dinosaur : Any animal belonging to a group of large reptiles that lived in the Mesozoic era. Scientists think modern birds are descendants of Mesozoic dinosaurs.

ichthyosaur : An extinct marine reptile that lived in the Mesozoic era. Icthyosaurus had a dolphin-shaped body and a narrow, tooth-filled 'beak."

ichthyosaurus (ik-thee-uh-SAWR-uhs)

La Brea (luh BRAY-uh)

Mesozoic (meh-zuh-ZOH-ihk)

mosasaur (MOH-zuh-sawr) : An extinct marine reptile that lived in the Mesozoic era. Mosasaur had a long head, a large jaw, a strong and flexible neck, and two strong pairs of paddles.

oviraptor (oh-vih-RAP-tur) : A small, bird-like dinosaur that moved quickly on its two long legs. Oviraptor had a long tail, a curved neck, powerful jaws, and a strong beak.

plesiosaur (PLEE-see-uh-sawr) : An extinct marine reptile that lived in the Mesozoic era. Mary Anning, a female fossil collector, found the first plesiosaur fossil.

protoceratops (proh-toh-SEHR-uh-tahps)

pterosaur (TEHR-uh-sawr)

velociraptor (vuh-LAH-suh-rap-tuhr) : An extinct marine reptile that lived in the Mesozoic era. The velociraptor was a particularly vicious dinosaur.

TEACH
Activity 1: Let's Read! *(Online)*
Instructions
Have your student read pages 36 to 45 to learn about the events and the incredible variety of organisms that existed in the Mesozoic and Cenozoic eras.

Activity 2: When Did It Happen? *(Offline)*
Instructions
Print out the When Did It Happen? sheet if you have not already done so. Encourage your student to refer to the book often as she answers the questions.

ASSESS
Lesson Assessment: The Mesozoic and Cenozoic Eras (*Online*)
Students will complete an online assessment based on the lesson objectives. The assessment will be scored by the computer. The attached answer key is the most current and may not coincide with previously printed guides.

TEACH
Activity 3. Optional: Were There Dinosaurs in Your Backyard? *(Online)*
Instructions
Scientists think that dinosaurs once lived in many parts of the word. Have your student visit Discovery Channel's *When Dinosaurs Roamed America* to see whether dinosaurs may have lived in her neighborhood.

Name _____   Date _____

When Did It Happen?

Some of these events happened in the Mesozoic Era, while others happened in the Cenozoic Era. Write an M next to each description that fits the Mesozoic Era, and write a C next to each description that fits the Cenozoic Era.

1.	Humans use fire for cooking.	C
2.	Pangaea breaks apart.	M
3.	Land animals begin to have live babies instead of laying eggs.	M
4.	Continents move toward their current locations.	C
5.	Dinosaurs live and roam the Earth.	M
6.	Animals get stuck in LaBrea Tar Pits.	C
7.	Temperature drops worldwide.	C
8.	Plesiosaurs and oviraptors live.	M
9.	Ice forms at north and south poles.	C
10.	The first large forests and open woodlands develop.	M
11.	Early humans make tools.	C
12.	A mass extinction occurs.	M

For each of these sets of events, scientific evidence suggests which happened first, second, and last. Put the events in order by writing 1, 2, or 3 in the spaces provided.

13. A. Dinosaurs come into being.   2
    B. Birds come into being.   3
    C. Animals similar to crocodiles
       learn to run on their hind legs.   1

14. A. Humans settle down to live in
       communities.   3
    B Organisms adapt to colder
      environments.   2
    C. Sea levels drop, exposing more land. 1

Learning Coach Guide
Lesson 6: Unit Review and Assessment

Your student will play a game and review what she learned throughout the unit. A Unit Assessment will follow the review activity.

Lesson Objectives

- State that fossils provide evidence that many kinds of organisms that once lived on Earth are now extinct.
- Name one major event that occurred in each of the four geologic sections: Precambrian, Paleozoic, Mesozoic, and Cenozoic.
- Describe the conditions under which fossils may form and distinguish among the different types, such as petrified, mold, and cast.
- Explain that fossils provide information about organisms that lived long ago and help scientists reconstruct the history of life on Earth.
- Recognize that scientists divide geologic time into four main sections (Precambrian, Paleozoic, Mesozoic, and Cenozoic) and that each section covers one major stage in Earth's history.

PREPARE

Approximate lesson time is 60 minutes.

Materials

For the Student

    ⌸ Fossils and Geologic Time Review Cards

    Come Learn with Me: The Fossil Record and the History of Life by Bridget Anderson

---

TEACH
Activity 1: Review the Book (Offline)
Instructions

Your student will use the book and any activity sheets from the unit to find the answers to the questions.

This is the answer key for the activity:

Question: I am a supercontinent. I formed during the Paleozoic era and broke apart in the Mesozoic era. What am I?

Answer: Pangea

Question: I am a fossil. I am made of dead wood that has hardened into stone. What kind of fossil am I?

Answer: petrified

Question: I am an era in geologic time. In this time, humans created tools and formed communities. Which era am I?

Answer: Cenozoic

Question: The Earth was just a ball of gases and hot lava when I began. Later, cyanobacteria filled the water. Which period of geological time am I?

Answer: Precambrian

Question: When a rock hardens inside a mold fossil, I am formed. What kind of fossil am I?

Answer: cast

Question: Velociraptors, proceratopses, and other dinosaurs roamed the Earth during my time period. Which era am I?

Answer: Mesozoic

Question: I hold an imprint of the shape and texture of something ancient. I may have been mud that has hardened into stone. What kind of fossil am I?

Answer: mold

Question: I provide evidence of organisms that are now extinct. By studying me, scientists can reconstruct the history of the Earth. What am I?

Answer: fossil

ASSESS
Unit Assessment: Fossils and Geologic Time (*Offline*)

Students will complete an offline Unit Assessment. Print the assessment and have students complete it on their own. Use the answer key to score the assessment, and then enter the results online. The attached answer key is the most current and may not coincide with previously printed guides.

TEACH
Activity 2. Optional: ZlugQuest Measurement (*Online*)

Name _____   Date _____

Unit Assessment Answer Key

Read each question and circle the letter next to the correct answer.

1. Which of these events occurred during the Precambrian time?
   A. Pangaea, the super continent, was formed.
   Ⓑ Cyanobacteria filled the water and air with oxygen.
   C. Pangaea began to break apart into many continents separated by shallow seas.
   D. Early humans began to make tools, harvest plants, and make cave paintings.

2. Which of these events occurred during the Paleozoic era?
   Ⓐ Pangaea, the super continent, was formed.
   B. Cyanobacteria filled the water and air with oxygen.
   C. Pangaea began to break apart into many continents separated by shallow seas.
   D. Early humans began to make tools, harvest plants, and make cave paintings.

3. Which of these events occurred during the Mesozoic era?
   A. Pangaea, the super continent, was formed.
   B. Cyanobacteria filled the water and air with oxygen.
   Ⓒ Pangaea began to break apart into many continents separated by shallow seas.
   D. Early humans began to make tools, harvest plants, and make cave paintings.

4. Which of these events occurred during the Cenozoic era?
   A. Pangaea, the super continent, was formed.
   B. Cyanobacteria filled the water and air with oxygen.
   C. Pangaea began to break apart into many continents separated by shallow seas.
   Ⓓ Early humans began to make tools, harvest plants, and make cave paintings.

<u>Name</u>   <u>Date</u>

Unit Assessment Answer Key

5. Scientists divide time into four main sections. Two sections are the Precambrian and the Paleozoic. What are the other two sections?
   A. Triassic and Cenzoic
   B. Pennsylvanian and Mesozoic
   C. Ice Age and Precambrian
   (D) Cenozoic and Mesozoic

6. Which type of fossil can be described as dead wood that has turned into stone?
   A. cast fossil
   B. mold fossil
   C. sedimentary fossil
   (D) petrified

7. Which type of fossil is an imprint made by an organism that was preserved in rock?
   A. cast fossil
   (B) mold fossil
   C. sedimentary fossil
   D. petrified

8. Which type of fossil is formed when a rock hardens inside a mold fossil?
   (A) cast fossil
   B. mold fossil
   C. sedimentary fossil
   D. petrified

Unit Assessment Answer Key

9. TRUE or FALSE: Fossils provide evidence that many kinds of organisms that are now extinct once lived on Earth.
    (A) True
    B. False

10. TRUE or FALSE: Fossils provide information about organisms that lived long ago and help scientists reconstruct the history of life on Earth.
    (A) True
    B. False

Learning Coach Guide
Lesson 7: Semester Review and Assessment

From invertebrates to electricity to the Earth and its past, you have learned a lot of science this semester. Review what you have learned as you prepare to take the second semester assessment.

Lesson Objectives

- Demonstrate mastery of the semester's content.
- Demonstrate mastery of the skills taught in this unit.
- Identify death and emigration as the two main factors that cause a decrease in a population.
- Explain that fossils provide information about organisms that lived long ago.
- State that a *fossil* is a trace, print, or remain of an organism preserved over time in a rock.
- Identify the conditions under which fossils may form.
- Explain that fossils help scientists reconstruct the history of life on Earth.
- State that fossils provide evidence that many kinds of organisms that once lived on Earth are now extinct.
- Identify the different types of fossils, such as petrified, cast, and mold.
- State that geologic time is divided into four sections: Precambrian, Paleozoic, Mesozoic, and Cenozoic.
- Recognize that scientists think that many kinds of organisms once lived on Earth have completely disappeared.
- Recognize that scientists think that some organisms alive today resemble organisms of the distant past.
- Name one major event that occurred during the Precambrian time.
- Name one major event that occurred during the Paleozoic era.
- Name one organism that lived on the Earth during the Precambrian time.
- Name one organism that lived on the Earth during the Paleozoic era.
- Name one major event that occurred during the Mesozoic era.
- Name one major event that occurred during the Cenozoic era.
- Name one organism that lived on the Earth during the Mesozoic era.
- Name one major event that occurred in each of the four geologic sections: Precambrian, Paleozoic, Mesozoic, and Cenozoic.
- Describe the conditions under which fossils may form and distinguish among the different types, such as petrified, mold, and cast.
- Explain that fossils provide information about organisms that lived long ago and help scientists reconstruct the history of life on Earth.
- Recognize that scientists divide geologic time into four main sections (Precambrian, Paleozoic, Mesozoic, and Cenozoic) and that each section covers one major stage in Earth's history.
- Identify characteristics of sponges (they have the ability to regenerate damaged parts, they reproduce through budding, and they live only in water).
- Identify a characteristic of cnidarians (they have tentacles with stinging cells).
- Identify characteristics of roundworms (they bend from side to side to move, have nostrils but no eyes).

- Identify characteristics of mollusks (they have a soft body, a thick skin called a mantle, and a foot for movement).
- Identify common characteristics of arthropods (they have jointed legs, a segmented body, and an exoskeleton).
- Identify characteristics of echinoderms (they are protected by hard plates, their body has radial symmetry, and they move by pumping water into their tube feet).
- Recognize that objects with the same electrical charges repel and objects with different electrical charges attract.
- Explain how to construct a temporary magnet.
- State that electric currents flow easily through materials that are conductors and do not flow easily through materials that are insulators.
- State that electric current produces magnetic fields and that an electromagnet can be made by wrapping a wire around a piece of iron and then running electricity through the wire.
- Identify the four main layers of the Earth and describe their characteristics.
- Recognize that you can identify minerals by their color, luster, hardness, streak, and specific gravity.
- Identify the three different types of rocks and how they form.
- Identify the main parts of a volcano: magma chamber, vent, and crater.
- Identify and describe the three types of land volcanoes (cinder cone, composite, and shield).
- State that an *earthquake* is the shaking or sliding of the Earth's surface.
- Describe a soil profile and explain how different horizons are formed.
- Explain both the physical and the chemical weathering of rocks, and be able to classify examples of each.
- Demonstrate that magnets have two poles (north and south) and that like poles repel each other while unlike poles attract each other.

PREPARE

Approximate lesson time is 60 minutes.

Advance Preparation

- If you don't already have it, you will need the books *Come Learn With Me: Animals Without Backbones - Invertebrates* and *Come Learn With Me: Fossil Record and the History of Life* by Bridget Anderson for the required Explore activity in this lesson.

TEACH
Activity 1: Semester Review *(Online)*
Instructions
Have your student read through the semester review. Reinforce and explain difficult concepts as needed. Revisit any specific lessons that may have been difficult during the semester.

ASSESS

Semester Assessment: Science 4, Semester Two *(Offline)*
Students will complete an offline Semester assessment. Print the assessment and have students complete it on their own. Use the answer key to score the assessment, and then enter the results online. The attached answer key is the most current and may not coincide with previously printed guides.

Name _____ Date _____

Semester Assessment Answer Key

Study the pictures below. In each picture, a type of physical or chemical weathering is taking place. Under each picture, write the name of what is causing the weathering or erosion to occur (water, wind, acids, or glaciers) and whether it is an example of physical or chemical weathering.

1. kind of weathering _____ **chemical** _____

    What caused the erosion? _____ **acid** _____

2. kind of weathering _____ **physical** _____

    What caused the erosion? _____ **wind** _____

3. kind of weathering _____ **physical** _____

    What caused the erosion? _____ **water** _____

4. kind of weathering _____ **physical** _____

    What caused the erosion? _____ **glacier** _____

Semester Assessment Answer Key

Circle the correct answers for questions 5 – 17.

5. What is name of the towering volcanoes that form from both lava flows and cinder rocks?
   A. cinder cone volcanoes
   B. composite volcanoes
   C. mountain volcanoes
   D. shield volcanoes

6. Scientists divide time into four main sections. Two sections are the Precambrian and the Paleozoic. What are the other two sections?
   A. Triassic and Cenozoic
   B. Pennsylvanian and Mesozoic
   C. Ice Age and Precambrian
   D. Cenozoic and Mesozoic

7. What will happen when the north pole of a magnet is placed against the south pole of another magnet?
   A. The poles will attract each other.
   B. Both magnets will start to spin.
   C. The poles will repel each other.
   D. Both magnets will flip to the opposite side.

8. Which layer of the Earth is extremely hot and made almost entirely of solid iron?
   A. outer core
   B. crust
   C. inner core
   D. mantle

9. What is the tube-like part of a volcano called that lava flows through during an eruption?
   A. magma chamber
   B. cinder cone
   C. crater
   D. vent

Semester Assessment Answer Key

10. Earthquakes happen around the world and can cause landslides, cracks in the ground, or damage to buildings and roads. Which of the following causes earthquakes?
    A. giant ocean waves called tsunamis
    (B.) underground movement of earth's plates
    C. energy released from a volcano
    D. problems in the air that make earth unbalanced

11. Scientists can identify common minerals by testing their physical properties. Circle all of the tests that scientists use to do this.
    (A.) color
    B. smoothness
    (C.) streak
    (D.) luster
    E. solubility
    (F.) hardness

12. True or (False) A cast fossil is formed when a rock hardens inside a petrified fossil.

13. (True) or False: An iron nail can be made magnetic by wrapping it in wire and sending electricity through it.

14. True or (False) A needle rubbed with a magnet becomes a permanent magnet.

15. True or (False) The crust is the thick, soft, smooth outer layer of the Earth.

16. (True) or False: The outer core is mostly made of liquid iron.

17. True or (False) A cinder cone volcano is formed when lava comes up out of the ground very quickly.

Semester Assessment Answer Key

Use the words in the Word Bank to complete the sentences below.

chamber	cast	attract
insulators	repel	magnetic
mantle	petrified	profile
inner core	conductors	

18. Objects with the same electrical charges _____**repel**_____, while those with different electric charges _____**attract**_____.

19. Conductors are materials that electric currents flow easily through. Electric currents do not flow easily through _____**insulators**_____.

20. Electric currents produce _____**magnetic**_____fields.

21. If you dig a deep hole in the surface of the Earth, you would see different layers that have formed as a result of many years of weathering. The layers make up the soil _____**profile**_____.

22. A _____**petrified**_____fossil is dead wood that has turned into stone.

23. The _____**mantle**_____is located between the outer core and the crust. It is made of solid rock, but is under so much pressure that it is constantly moving.

24. The central collecting place for magma at the base of a volcano is called the magma _____**chamber**_____.

Semester Assessment Answer Key

25. Match the groups of invertebrates to their descriptions.

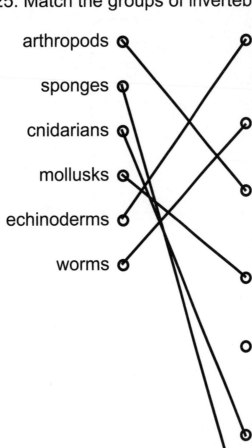

arthropods

sponges

cnidarians

mollusks

echinoderms

worms

Protected by hard plates, these animals' bodies show radial symmetry. They pump water into their tube-like feet to move.

These animals have nostrils, but no eyes. They bend from side to side to move.

The bodies of these animals are segmented and covered in a hard exoskeleton. They have jointed legs.

Thick skin covers these animals' soft bodies. They have a foot that is used for movement.

These animals have hair and fur to cover their bodies. They also regulate their body temperatures.

The ocean is home to these animals. They have tentacles coming from their bodies with long, stinging cells on the ends.

These animals are only found in water. They reproduce through budding and have the ability to regenerate a damaged body part.

Semester Assessment Answer Key

Igneous, sedimentary and metamorphic are the three types of rock found on Earth. Describe each type of rock below and how it is formed.

26. igneous: _____

_____ **Answers may vary but should include: Igneous rocks form in** _____

_____ **volcanoes and wherever magma pushes through the crust of** _____

_____ **the earth.** _____

27. sedimentary: _____

_____ **Answers may vary but should include: Sedimentary rocks form** _____

_____ **when bits of rock are compacted by pressure and cement together** _____

_____ **to form new rocks.** _____

_____

28. metamorphic: _____

_____ **Answers may vary but should include: Metamorphic rocks form** _____

_____ **when other rocks are subjected to large amounts of pressure, heat,** _____

_____ **or chemical reactions.** _____

_____

_____